School-based Assessments and Interventions for ADD Students

James M. Swanson, Ph.D.

Contents

PART I: BACKGROUND

PART II: ASSESSMENT

4. THE SNAP RATING SCALE

5. THE CLAM RATING SCALE

6. THE SKAMP RATING SCALE

7. DIRECT OBSERVATIONS

PART III: INTERVENTION

8. EDUCATIONAL INTERVENTIONS

9. UCI-CDC PROCEDURES

10. Programs at UCI-CDC

PART I: BACKGROUND

1. INTRODUCTION

1.1 Psychiatric Definition of ADD

Since 1980, the psychiatric definition of Attention Deficit Disorder (ADD) has been used by most professionals, including pediatricians, psychologists, and educators as well as psychiatrists. A perplexing array of psychiatric definitions have been offered in 3 versions of the Diagnostic and Statistical Manual (DSM) of the American Psychiatric Association:

> • Attention Deficit Disorder (ADD) and Attention Deficit Disorder with Hyperactivity (ADD+H) were defined in DSM-III (1980).
>
> • Attention Deficit Hyperactivity Disorder (ADHD) and Undifferentiated ADD (UADD) were defined in DSM-III-Revised (R) (1987).
>
> • Attention Deficit Hyperactivity Disorder (ADHD) and Attention Deficit Disorder without Hyperactivity (ADD-H) have been suggested in DSM-IV Options Book: Work in Progress (WIP) (1991).

The DSM approach has produced excellent definitions of ADD for psychiatry. But, as pointed out in DSM-III-R (1987, p. xxiv), "It should be understood, however, that for most of the categories the diagnostic criteria are based on clinical judgement, and have not yet been fully validated by data about such important correlates as clinical course, outcome, family history, and treatment response. Undoubtedly, with further study the criteria will be further refined."

The DSM-IV Task Force, appointed by the American Psychiatric Association, is working to identify the most pertinent questions regarding the diagnostic utility, reliability, and descriptive validity of the ADD diagnosis, including the provisions for subtypes such as ADD with (ADD+H) and without (ADD-H) Hyperactivity. The Task Force (DSM-IV-WIP, 1991) is conducting a "... three-stage process of empirical review that includes: 1) comprehensive and systematic reviews of the published literature, 2) analyses of already-collected but not previously analyzed data, and 3) field trials" (p. A:3).

When the final version of DSM-IV becomes available in 1993, the psychiatric definition of ADD should be set for the next decade. Apparently (DSM-IV-WIP, 1991) the definition will be based on two sets of symptoms:

> • **Inattention**: easily distracted, difficulty following through on instructions, difficulty sustaining attention, does not seem to listen, loses things, fails to give close attention to details, difficulty organizing goal-directed activities, shifts from one uncompleted activity to another.
>
> • **Hyperactivity-Impulsivity**: leaves seat in classroom, difficulty awaiting turn, blurts out answers to questions, difficulty playing quietly, runs about or climbs on things excessively, engages in physically dangerous activity, fidgets or squirms in seat, interrupts or intrudes on others.

To meet the criteria for ADHD proposed in DSM-IV-WIP (1991), the pattern of behavior described by these symptoms must be developmentally inappropriate. The exact number of symptoms required for a diagnosis has not yet been set.

4

1.2 An Educational Definition of ADD

In addition to a sound psychiatric definition of ADD, an educational definition is needed. A psychiatric definition of ADD is evaluated by data from important clinical correlates such as response to medical treatment and clinical course of the disorder (DSM-III-R, 1987). Similarly, an educational definition should be evaluated by data from important educational correlates such as response to academic intervention and progress in school. The educational and psychiatric interventions and outcomes of ADD are quite different, and to take this into account different definitions are needed.

To recognize these differences, an educational definition of ADD has been developed to complement rather than replace the psychiatric definition. The Professional Group for Attention and Related Disorders (PGARD) offered the following educational definition (see Appendix A):

"The condition 'attention deficit disorder' refers to a developmental disorder involving one or more of the basic cognitive processes related to orienting, focusing or maintaining attention, resulting in a marked degree of inadequate attention to academic and social tasks. The disorder may also include verbal or motor impulsivity and excessive non-task related activities such as fidgeting or restlessness. The inattentive behavior of ADD most commonly has onset in early childhood, remains inappropriate for age, and persists throughout development.

ADD adversely affects educational performance to the extent that a significant discrepancy exists between a child's intellectual ability and that child's productivity with respect to listening, following directions, planning, organizing, or completing academic assignments which require reading, writing, spelling, or mathematical calculations.

Inattentive behaviors, if caused by cultural differences, socioeconomic disadvantage, or lack of adequate exposure to the language of educational instruction, are not evidence of ADD. Inattentive behaviors with acute onset are not evidence of ADD if they arise directly from (1) stressful events associated with family functioning (e.g., parental divorce, or the death of a family member or a close friend) or environmental disruption (e.g., a change in residence or school); (2) post-traumatic stress reactions caused by abuse (e.g., physical, psychological, or sexual) or natural disasters; (3) noncompliance due solely to opposition or defiance; (4) frustration resulting from inappropriate tasks beyond intellectual ability or level of achievement skills; or (5) emotional disorders (e.g., anxiety, depression, schizophrenia).

ADD can coexist with other handicapping conditions (i.e., specific learning disabilities, serious emotional disturbance, or mental retardation).

The following definitions are given for the terms stated above:

1. 'a marked degree' means, at a minimum, disproportionate for the child's age as measured by well-standardized and unbiased rating scales or structured interviews, resulting in functional impairment.

2. 'onset in early childhood' means that when a careful developmental history of the child is obtained, it confirms that parents, teachers or other involved adults have observed the development of the age-inappropriate inattentive behaviors before the age of 7 years. The onset of these persistent inattentive behaviors should not be confused with the educational manifestation of ADD, because onset of educational impairment may occur at any time in the child's life when school tasks tax the child's underlying attentional deficit."

The PGARD educational definition of ADD is based on criteria which are comparable to the criteria for other educational disabilities, such as Specific Learning Disability (SLD) or Serious Emotional Disturbance (SED), which have a long history of being listed in educational law (e.g., the Education for the Handicapped Act, PL 94-142) and have accepted educational definitions.

1.3 Background

The PGARD educational definition of ADD is based on a two-tier framework:

• First, the **clinical manifestation** of ADD must be confirmed by the presence and severity of specific symptoms (i.e., inattention, impulsivity, and hyperactivity), early onset and chronic duration of these symptoms, and consideration of exclusion criteria.

• Second, the **educational manifestation** of ADD must be documented, and evidence of impairment in school must be confirmed by adverse impact on performance in the classroom.

At the University of California Irvine Child Development Center (UCI-CDC), the educational aspect of ADD have been emphasized over the past decade. Specific educational assessments and interventions have been developed and refined in the context of research and clinical service delivered in an academic environment. The UCI-CDC methods represent tested ways to provide specific school-based assessments and interventions for ADD students.

Some background on the development of the UCI-CDC methods will be presented in Part I of this book. Five years of experience at the Hospital for Sick Children (HSC) in Toronto and 12 years of experience at the University of California, Irvine (UCI) provide the basis for the author's views presented in this book.

The UCI-CDC clinical assessment procedures were based on methods developed at the HSC during 5 years of work (1975 to 1980) with Marcel Kinsbourne, M.D. In 1980, the methods developed at the HSC were transferred to UCI and were used to establish an ADD assessment clinic. Intensive Summer treatment programs were initiated at UCI in 1982, based on a collaboration with William Pelham, Ph.D. This method of clinical intervention continued until 1985 when the UCI Child Development Center (UCI-CDC) was established.

In 1985, a year-round educational program for ADD students was initiated at the UCI-CDC, based on a collaboration with Steve Simpson, M.A., a school psychologist for the Orange County Department of Education (OCDE), the umbrella organization for 28 school districts in the county. A public school was set up on the UCI campus to develop intensive school-based interventions combined with comprehensive clinical interventions. The UCI-CDC school-based intervention programs evolved over several years, based on collaboration between a **clinical staff** from UCI (James Swanson, Ph.D., Ron Kotkin, Ph.D., Linda Pfiffner, Ph.D., Marc Lerner, M.D., Dave Agler, Dan Flynn, and Julie Elliot) and an **educational staff** from OCDE (Steve Simpson, Paul Corso, Larry Holcombe, Cheryl Rosenau, Kelly Mayfield, and Leila Ferrari).

In 1989, based on collaboration with Bruce Givner, an Assistant Superintendent of the Irvine Unified School District (IUSD), a pilot transition program was initiated to place ADD students completing the UCI-CDC school-based program temporarily in a regular school setting at El Toro Elementary School. In the context of this transition program, the UCI-CDC methods were modified to provide school-based intervention in regular classrooms for ADD children identified by the school.

Over the past decade, the applied clinical and educational programs at UCI-CDC were facilitated by research grants from the MacArthur Foundation (in collaboration with Eric Taylor, M.D. from the Institute of Psychiatry in London), the Educational Foundation of America, the Irvine Health Foundation, and the National Institute of Mental Health (in collaboration with Dennis Cantwell, M.D. from UCLA).

Current research efforts at UCI-CDC still emphasize the educational aspects of ADD. In 1991, one of the 4 ADD Centers established by the US Department of Education was awarded to the UCI-CDC. The initial focus of this ADD Center is to conduct a rigorous synthesis of the literature on medical interventions with ADD children. This project will be completed in 1993, and information from it will be distributed by the US Department of Education.

In 1992, UCI-CDC was selected as 1 of 6 sites for the National Institute of Mental Health (NIMH) Multimodality Treatment Study of ADD, based on a proposal written by James Swanson, Ph.D., Dennis Cantwell, M.D., Tim Wigal, Ph.D., Steve Simpson, M.A., James Satterfield, M.D., Breena Satterfield, M.A., Linda Pfiffner, Ph.D., Keith McBurnett, Ph.D, and Marc Lerner, M.D. A common research protocol, which will include combinations of clinical and educational interventions, will be developed in late 1992 and early 1993 for use across 6 collaborating sites. In September, 1993 the common research protocol will be initiated to evaluate the long-term effects of multimodality treatment for ADD.

The UCI-CDC assessment and intervention procedures are based on the author's involvement in these clinical, educational, and research programs, but the information presented in this book represent the author's own interpretation and modification of the UCI-CDC methods.

1.4 Purposes of This Book

This book has 3 purposes. The first purpose of this book is **to help educators understand and respond to the new Federal guidelines about ADD.** The responsibilities of the public schools for the assessment and intervention with ADD students changed dramatically in 1991 when the Department of Education recognized ADD as a potentially handicapping or disabling condition (Davila et al., 1991). Effective parent groups, Children with Attention Deficit Disorder (CHADD) and the Attention Deficit Disorder Associations (ADDA), were responsible for initiating these changes, which were made over the objections of many national organizations for educators. A description of the grass roots legislative action of these parent groups will be presented to explain why the Federal guidelines about ADD changed abruptly in 1991.

The second purpose of this book is **to present the assessment methods which have been evolving at UCI-CDC since 1985.** Certainly, as described above, the development of these methods has been a team effort involving many individuals from several professions. The results are described in some detail in published articles about the UCI-CDC programs (Swanson, 1988; Swanson et al., 1990). However, these articles are in a format for academic communication that makes them difficult to interpret and to use in educational applications. In the Part II of this book, the assessment strategies from these academic communications are presented in formats for educators.

The third purpose of this book is **to present specific intervention methods currently in use the UCI-CDC**. Educators have the difficult task of implementing the new Federal guidelines about ADD in the face of financial constraints at the State and local levels. Information about the speciality programs at the UCI-CDC will be presented in Part III. This material may help educators effectively use scarce educational resources to meet their new responsibilities for ADD students.

This book is not intended to be a comprehensive manual. Only school-based methods are presented here. Traditionally, most methods for assessments and interventions for ADD children have emphasized work with parents in the home or clinicians in a medical setting. A wealth of material exists (see Barkley, 1990) which will not be repeated here. This book is intended to be an introductory manual covering a limited set of basic principles and techniques which can be used to build complex assessments and interventions for ADD students in the public schools. Information is presented in 3 parts of this book:

In Part I, the new regulations (Chapter 2) and general methods (Chapter 3) will be presented.

In Part II, 3 ADD rating scales -- the SNAP-IV (Chapter 4), the CLAM (Chapter 5), and the SKAMP (Chapter 6) -- will be presented, followed by a description of direct observation methods (Chapter 7).

In Part III, background on behavioral interventions will be presented (Chapters 8) and the UCI-CDC applications for school-based interventions will be described (Chapters 9 and 10).

2. LEGISLATION AND REGULATIONS

2.1 Legislation and ADD

In 1990, Public Law 94-142, the Education for the Handicapped Act (EHA), was amended and renamed the Individuals with Disabilities Education Act (IDEA). This process started quietly in 1989, when the Senate passed its version of a bill (S. 1824) to reauthorize the EHA. S. 1824 did not address the ADD issue. The process became more controversial in 1990, when the House of Representatives conducted hearings which included testimony about ADD. As part of this part of this process, professionals and parents addressed the House of Representatives Committee on Education and Labor. After verbal testimony, the Committee asked for written responses to 4 questions:

- Does ADD exist as a recognizable disorder?

- What is the prevalence of ADD?

- Are ADD children being served under the EHA?

- What services should the public schools provide?

Lengthy written responses were prepared by CHADD, ADDA, and PGARD. The PGARD testimony, included as Appendix B of this book, expressed the views that ADD is a bona fide disorder, that its prevalence is relatively low, that ADD students were not being well served under the EHA, and that specific educational interventions for ADD students could be implemented in the public schools.

Apparently, these views were convincing: the House bill (H.R. 1013) modified the EHA definition of one of the existing categories of handicapping condition, Other Health Impaired (OHI), to include a specific reference to ADD.

The action of the House of Representatives to recognized ADD was very simple. H.R. 1013 stated in Sec. 602. (a) the following definition:

"1) The term "children with disabilities" means children--
(A) with mental retardation, hearing impairments including deafness, speech or language impairments, visual impairments including blindness, serious emotional disturbance, orthopedic impairments, autism, traumatic brain injury, other health impairments including attention deficit disorder, or specific learning disabilities; and
(B) who, by reason thereof, need special education and related services."

The 4 words, *including attention deficit disorder,* created quite a commotion. This proposed recognition of ADD was a surprise and apparently was quite disturbing to national educational organizations which had headquarters and staff in Washington, D.C.

If accepted, H.R. 1013 would have given ADD legal status equivalent to that of existing handicapping categories of the EHA (now called disability categories in the IDEA), such as Specific Learning Disability (SLD) and Serious Emotional Disturbance (SED). Most organizations representing educators opposed the introduction of a new category for designating an educationally handicapping (or disabling) condition.

To resolve the differences in H.R. 1013 and S. 1824, the IDEA reauthorization bill went to a Conference Committee. Several national organizations of educators (e.g., the National Association of State Directors of Special Education, the National School Boards Association, the American Association of School Administrators, the Council for Exceptional Children, the National Association of School Psychologists, the National Association of Secondary School Principals, and others) made presentations to the Conference Committee to **oppose** the recognition of ADD in H.R. 1013.

Because of concern about the scientific acceptability of some information presented to the Conference Committee, staff from Senator Harkin's office (Bobby Silverstein and Ira Shoulson) arranged a meeting between members of the Professional Group for Attention and Related Disorders (PGARD) and staff members of the Senate Subcommittee on Disability Policy. Russell Barkley, Benjamin Lahey, Bennett Shaywitz, Alan Zametkin, and James Swanson provided reviews of the literature about the differences between ADD and LD (Shaywitz), the biological basis of ADD (Zametkin), current diagnostic issues (Lahey), long-term educational outcome (Barkley), and school-based intervention (Swanson).

During this period of critical legislative action, a coalition of leaders from CHADD and ADDA (Sandy Thomas, Pamela Murray, Mary Fowler, Harvey Parker, Nancy Cornish, Nancy Eisenberg, Debra Maxey, Fran Rice, and others) engaged in heroic efforts to present a case in favor of H.R. 1013. However, these efforts were not sufficient to change S. 1824. In the final version, the reference to ADD in H.R. 1013 was removed, and when the EHA was reauthorized as the IDEA, the statutory definition of ADD was not changed.

2.2 The Notice of Inquiry

Even though Congress did not change the law about ADD, these discussions raised the awareness of Congress about the disorder. The representatives of ADDA and CHADD vigorously continued a dialogue with Congressional leaders and their staff members. This persistence paid off by convincing Congress to seek more information about ADD.

Instead of dismissing the ADD issue, Congress issued a **Notice of Inquiry on ADD** in the Federal Register on Nov. 29, 1990. This represented an official fact-finding effort to obtain input from a wide variety of sources about ADD and to evaluate the adequacy of educational law and educational practices concerning ADD.

The Notice of Inquiry directed the US Department of Education to solicit input about ADD and to report on 10 specific questions. Over 2000 responses were received and processed. One of these responses was from PGARD. To make that response more accessible to educators, the Executive Summary is included as Appendix A of this book.

The 10 questions of the Notice of Inquiry are presented in a paraphrased and condensed version here:

• Are ADD children being excluded from special education services under current law (the EHA)?

• Are ADD children currently being identified under other disability categories?

• Do ADD children have unique characteristics not reflected in existing disability categories?

• What educational services are school districts currently proving for ADD students?

• How should ADD be described operationally for qualifying a child for special education services?

• What specific manifestations of ADD should be included in this educational definition?

• Should the educational definition specify circumstances which produce transient inattentive behavior?

• Should the educational definition of ADD address its concurrence with LD and SED?

• Should guidelines be provided to State and local educational agencies regarding how to evaluate ADD?

• Who should be authorized to conduct an assessment of a child suspected of having ADD?

• What provisions are necessary in the ADD definition to avoid misclassification of minority students?

2.3 The PGARD Response

A group of PGARD members, including James Swanson, Russell Barkley, Sidney Zentall, James Satterfield, and Lewis Bloomingdale, worked diligently with representatives of CHADD and ADDA to prepare a **comprehensive response to the Notice of Inquiry**. The PGARD response, which is public information and should be available from the US Department of Education, is a rich source of information about ADD. However, the complete PGARD response is rather long, and it is not a simple matter to obtain a copy of it. After 2 years, PGARD still receives requests for a photocopy of its response, and parts of it were recently published by CHADD (Fowler, 1992). The Executive Summary is included as Appendix A of this book.

The PGARD response offered recommendations for educational assessments and educational interventions for ADD students. In this book, these PGARD recommendations will be discussed and related to methods developed at the UCI-CDC over the past decade.

The PGARD response to the Notice of Inquiry proposed a two-tier educational assessment of ADD:

• Tier 1: An evaluation of **psychiatric symptoms** of ADD was recommended to be based on generally accepted clinical criteria (e.g., DSM-III, III-R, or IV).

• Tier 2: An evaluation of the **educational impact** of ADD was recommended to document adverse effects on academic performance and to determine the degree of impairment in the classroom setting.

The PGARD response to the Notice of Inquiry also proposed a three-level strategy for educational interventions:

• **Modifications in the regular classroom** were recommended which could be implemented by most teachers who were made aware of them. Suggested modifications included altered seating arrangements to facilitate teacher supervision and feedback, adjustment of the length of assignments, and increased teacher-parent communication concerning academic performance and behavior management.

• **Consultations with the teacher** were recommended to design, implement, and monitor specialized programs for ADD students. Suggested areas for consultation with a psychologist or resource specialist experienced with ADD included organizational techniques to bypass expected disorganization, homework assignment notebooks checked by teachers and parents, parent-teacher journals, interactive instead of didactic instructional techniques, and extra books for home.

• **Provisions for supplementary services** were recommended to facilitate the use of intensive behavior modification programs. Suggested techniques included sophisticated token reinforcement systems (to increase the quality, magnitude, timing, and consistency of consequences for work performance, adherence to rules, and prosocial behavior), daily report cards (to provide potent home-based reinforcements), skill training (in self-monitoring, self-evaluation, and self-instruction methods), and case management (to coordinate interventions across different settings and staff).

2.4 The ADD Memorandum

The Notice of Inquiry was not an insignificant exercise to appease the ADD proponents who did not succeed in changing educational law. Instead, the Notice of Inquiry convinced the US Department of Education to issue **a memorandum to change the interpretation of the regulations which implement the IDEA.** Since educational regulations have the same force as educational law, this has produced a profound effect on educational responsibilities and practices concerning ADD. A copy of this memorandum (Davila, Williams, and MacDonald, 1991) has been distributed to the Chief State School Officer of each state.

The former policy had stated "...that ADD is a characteristic of a specific learning disability or other handicapping condition, but is not itself a handicapping condition as defined in regulations implementing the EHA" (Bellamy, 1987, p. 472). The new policy states the following (bold type added):

> • ADD students may be considered disabled "...**solely on the basis of the disorder** within the 'other health impaired' category " (p. 3).
>
> • Public schools "...are required to have procedures for **locating, identifying and evaluating**" all ADD children, and this applies to all ADD children "...regardless of the severity of their disability" (p. 4).
>
> • If an ADD student is eligible under Part B of the IDEA, a "...**full continuum of placement alternatives, including the regular classroom,** must be available for providing special education and related services required in the IEP" (p. 3).

For these new Federal guidelines to be implemented by the States, new procedures will be required for the public schools to assess ADD students in the school setting and to intervene with a range of services to meet their educational needs.

The Federal action on ADD occurred so rapidly (compared to other changes in educational policy) that educators were not fully prepared to respond effectively. For that reason, the US Department of Education Office of Special Education Programs (OSEP) established 4 ADD Centers to organize, synthesize, and disseminate information about ADD. In addition, the Department of Education supported an effort by the Federal Resource Center at the University of Kentucky to identify and investigate promising practices which are already being applied to meet the needs of students with ADD.

Over time, this impressive effort by the US Department of Education should provide excellent information about school-based methods for assessments and interventions with ADD students in the public schools. However, at the present time very little information is available for directing educational assessments and interventions specifically for ADD students.

Since the UCI-CDC has emphasized educational aspects of ADD for several years, school-based assessment and intervention methods have already been developed and refined. This book was written to make these specific methods available to educators **now**, in order to help them meet the new responsibilities for educational assessment and intervention with ADD students in the public schools.

3. UCI-CDC METHODS

3.1 Preview

In 1980, a speciality clinic was established at the University of California Irvine (UCI) to provide clinical services for the assessment and treatment of ADD children. In 1985, this program evolved into the Child Development Center (CDC) with a facility on the university campus to house a small public school for ADD students. Over the past 12 years, methods for assessment and treatment of ADD children have been developed and tested in this clinic and school. This book presents adaptations of the UCI-CDC methods for use by educators.

The PGARD educational definition of ADD recommended **the use of teacher ratings as a primary source of information**. Three teacher rating scales have been developed at the UCI-CDC for use in an educational assessment of ADD students:

> • The latest version of the Swanson, Nolan, and Pelham (SNAP) rating scale consists of ADD items taken directly from the symptom lists of DSM-III (1980), DSM-III-R (1987), and DSM-IV:WIP (1991).
>
> • The Conners, Loney and Milich (CLAM) rating scale is based on dimensions of behavior rather than symptoms of a psychiatric disorder.
>
> • The Swanson, Kotkin, Agler, M-Flynn, and Pelham (SKAMP) rating scale is based on target behaviors specified in the UCI-CDC school-based behavior modification program.

The PGARD educational definition recognized different levels of severity of ADD which require different intensities of intervention. For the lowest severity level, modification of the classroom by a teacher or consultation with a psychologist to establish special programs (see Carlson and Lahey, 1988; Pfiffner and Barkley, 1990; Zentall, 1991) may offer sufficient interventions. Advice on how to achieve these first-level interventions in the typical public school setting has appeared in parent newsletters (i.e., CHADD's *Chadder* and ADDA's *Challenge*), in the CHADD Educators Manual (Fowler, 1992), and in a report of the Council for Exceptional Children (1992). For higher levels of severity of ADD, more intensive behavior therapy may be required. Several sources (e.g., O'Leary and O'Leary, 1977 or Kazdin, 1989) provide technical information on how to implement sophisticated behavior modification interventions for students with classroom problems.

This book was not designed to duplicate these excellent sources. Instead, it was designed to describe applications at UCI-CDC of the principles of operant conditioning and techniques of behavior modification **specifically for students with ADD**. Three general models will be described:

> • The **parallel teaching model** to alter the regular classroom to meet the needs of ADD students with mild impairments.
>
> • The **paraprofessional model** to supplement the regular classroom staff to meet the needs of ADD students with moderate impairments.
>
> • The **multicomponent model** to provide comprehensive clinical and educational interventions to meet the needs of ADD students with severe impairments.

3.2 Comprehensive Assessment

At the UCI-CDC, a comprehensive assessment of a referred child involves 3 professionals experienced with ADD:

• A **psychologist** collects information from direct observation, questionnaires, and interviews to evaluate the behavioral symptoms of the child and to recommend appropriate levels of behavioral intervention.

• A **pediatrician** collects information from physical and neurodevelopmental evaluations to rule out other medical disorders and to make decisions about treating the child with medication.

• A **psychometrician** collects information from IQ and achievement tests to evaluate the child for concurrent learning disabilities and to make recommendations for school placement or academic remediation.

At the UCI-CDC, a general questionnaire (e.g., the Achenbach Child Behavior Checklist) is used to screen for non-ADD problems and to help rule out internalizing disorders such as depression or anxiety. The psychometric assessment (i.e., based on IQ and achievement tests) is used to rule out low IQ or LD as primary causes of ADD-like masking symptoms of these underlying disorders.

The psychologist's assessment starts with parents and teachers completing an extensive set of questionnaires about the child. This is followed by a face-to-face interview with the parents and the child, as well as a telephone discussion in some instances with the teacher.

The parent interview focuses on the inclusion and exclusion criteria for ADD. This interview is structured and uses probe questions to systematically direct a discussion of each ADD symptom listed in the DSM-III, DSM-III-R, and DSM-IV-WIP manuals for the disruptive behavior disorders (ADD, ODD, and CD). **The psychologist uses the parent interview to filter information through clinical experience.**

The parent report of the child's behavior is interpreted by considering factors which are not well addressed by the impersonal nature of the questionnaire method (e.g., misunderstanding of items, individual differences in tolerance which affect the choice of rating responses, cultural or ethnic differences, etc.). An experienced clinician can use this method to impose a standard criterion across different cases to make judgements about the presence or absence of ADD symptoms.

The psychologist's judgement about each symptom, not the parent's Yes or No answer, is used to obtain a **symptom count** of the items. This symptom count is compared to the cutoff values stated for the number of symptoms required by various DSM criteria (i.e., III, III-R, or IV). This provides information for making categorical diagnoses (i.e., ADD and ADD+H in DSM-III (1980); ADHD in DSM-III-R (1987); a revised ADHD and ADD-H in DSM-IV-WIP (1991).

It is not recommended that an educational assessment of ADD duplicate the comprehensive UCI-CDC clinical assessment outlined above. Instead, part of the psychologist's assessment (described above) is recommended for use by school personnel. The UCI-CDC assessment methods, modified and adapted for this purpose, are presented in Part II of this book.

Even if ADD symptoms are present, a diagnosis of ADD may not be warranted. Other conditions may produce non-ADD masking symptoms (inattention, impulsivity, or overactivity) which hide an underlying condition such as anxiety, depression, LD, abuse, or stress. To help avoid making a diagnosis based on masking symptoms, consideration is recommended of the following characteristics of bona fide ADD symptoms:

> • **Early Onset.** As specified in DSM-III (1980), DSM-III-R (1987), and DSM-IV-WIP (1991), onset of ADD symptoms before the age of 7 is required.
>
> • **Persistent Presence.** ADD symptoms must be present over time (i.e., across stages of development) and be developmentally inappropriate at each stage.
>
> • **Functional Impairment.** The severity of ADD symptoms must be great enough to disrupt the daily activities of the child at school and at home.
>
> • **Primary Status.** The presence of ADD symptoms must precede the appearance of another comorbid disorder (e.g., LD, depression, or anxiety) instead of following the other disorder and being secondary to it.

All of these conditions should be verified before a diagnosis of ADD is made. For example, if a student's ADD symptoms appear suddenly at age 10, or were present only in kindergarten, or currently are present but do not interfere with other activities, or follow a history of LD, then the diagnosis of ADD is **not** recommended. An important part of the psychologist's assessment is to consider this sort of information that might rule out the ADD diagnosis. At the UCI-CDC clinic, these exclusion criteria rule out approximately 25% of the cases referred for assessment of ADD.

26

3.3 Teacher Rating Scales

In DSM-III (1980, p. 43), priority was given to teacher reports of ADD symptoms when the parent and teacher impressions differed. In DSM-IV-WIP (1991, p. C12) an option is being considered which would give priority to the presence of ADD symptoms in a **structured setting** such as the school environment. These priorities are based on the presumption that teachers can make better relative judgements about the behavior of students in structured settings because of experience with a large number of same-aged children and consequently a greater familiarity with **age-appropriate norms.**

These stated priorities for teacher reports emphasize the importance of developmentally inappropriate behavior in structured settings as diagnostic criteria for ADD. The requirement to document age-inappropriate behavior can be met by using age norms for ratings of ADD behavior, and the emphasis on a structured setting can be met by using a rating scale that specifically targets behavior during a classroom period. Three teacher rating scales described in detail in Part II of this book can be used to meet these requirements in the following ways:

> • The SNAP rating scale assesses the specific DSM-defined **psychiatric symptoms** of ADD.
>
> • The CLAM rating scale assesses severity of IOWA-defined **dimensions of behavior** related to ADD.
>
> • The SKAMP rating scale assesses the UCI-CDC-defined **educational impact of ADD** during a typical classroom period.

The SNAP rating scale is based on **psychiatric symptoms** of ADD as stated in the Diagnostic and Statistical Manuals (DSM-III, DSM-III-R, DSM-IV-WIP), and it provides a simple way to estimate severity of symptoms. An individual's score on a subscale of the SNAP rating scale can be compared to norms to establish a *marked degree* of inattention as recommend by the PGARD educational definition of ADD. Statistical abnormality can be defined by a subscale score greater than a specified value such as 2 Standard Deviations (SD) above the mean (M). **Using a statistical cutoff value on the SNAP provides a way to limit the proportion of students who meet the educational criteria for ADD.**

The CLAM rating scale is based on **dimensions of behavior** from the IOWA rating scale Loney and Milich, 1982). By comparing a student's score to norms for two independent dimensions of behavior, Inattention/Overactivity (I/O) and Aggression/Defiance (A/D), an individual usually can be placed in one of two subgroups: Pure ADD (without antisocial behavior) and Mixed ADD (with aggressive and defiant behavior). **Using the CLAM provides a way to establish these subgroups of ADD students.**

The SKAMP rating scale is based on **classroom behavior** specified in the UCI-CDC school-based token reinforcement program. The items are divided into two types (Attention and Deportment), and a time period is specified to evaluate a student's activities during a single class. Repeated assessment can be used to establish baselines for the specified subsets of behavior in the classroom. Regular reassessment with the SKAMP provides a way to monitor changes in these key target behaviors when consequences (e.g., tokens) are made contingent upon the presence of appropriate behavior or the absences of inappropriate behavior. **Using the SKAMP in this way provides a way to link assessment to intervention.**

3.4 Observations of Behavior

Teacher rating scales are based on **subjective impressions** of student behavior in the classroom. When specific rating scales are used systematically, this is an extremely efficient method for obtaining information about ADD symptoms.

For more objective information, **direct observations** of ADD behavior may be used to document or verify ADD symptoms,. The use of direct observation methods requires much more time and technical knowledge to implement than the use of rating scales.

At the UCI-CDC, direct observation methods are not emphasized. However, 2 protocols were selected from the literature, and descriptions are presented in Chapter 7. Each has an appropriate theoretical basis, established empirical support, and is easy to use. These protocols provide a structured way (without special equipment) to perform direct observations of ADD behavior in actual and analog school settings:

• The **Classroom Observation** of Conduct and Attention Deficit Disorders (COCADD) developed by Atkins, Pelham, and Licht (1985, 1988, 1989).

• The **Restricted Academic Setting** (RAS) developed by Roberts, Milich, and Loney (1984) and Roberts (1990).

The Roberts (1990) protocol measures attention to a laboratory task (such as a coding or cancellation test) rather than direct measures of performance on the test. Direct measures of performance are likely to be correlated with general ability and so would require adjustment for IQ before being used in the diagnostic process to evaluate ADD. Thus, to document the manifestations of ADD symptoms on a rote task (such as letter-digit coding), an attentional measures such as *Time On Task* may be better than a performance measure such as *Number of Digits Coded*. Commercial tests such as the GDS or the TOVA, which use performance measures based on a digit or letter monitoring task such as the Continuous Performance Task (CPT), may also require an adjustment for IQ for the same reasons.

Observational methods can be used to determine whether the symptoms of ADD are present at a particular point in time. They can also be used to determine to what degree ADD symptoms are present in a one-to-one setting. In this limited way, direct observations can provide information about the inclusion criteria for ADD. However, it is important to note that direct observation methods do not address exclusion criteria. **Exclusion criteria are critically important, because many transient and non-ADD conditions may disrupt a child's behavior in the classroom and impair performance on these tasks.**

Non-ADD factors such as parental divorce, economic deprivation, death in the family, lack of exposure to the language used for classroom instruction, etc.) should be considered when direct observations are used. Disruption of a child's attention or deportment in school due to these factors should not be taken as evidence for a diagnosis of ADD.

3.5 Cultural and Ethnic Factors

The PGARD response to the Notice of Inquiry emphasized the need for consideration of ethnic and cultural factors in the diagnosis of ADD. In the past, certain disability categories (i.e., Serious Emotional Disturbance and Educable Mental Retardation) have been used to overidentify children from ethnic and cultural minorities. Legal action was taken to prevent this misuse of these categories, but apparently the SLD disability category has been substituted for the same purpose (Dent, 1992).

Legitimate concern has been expressed about the possible misuse of the ADD label in a similar fashion.

The PGARD response to the Notice of Inquiry noted that epidemiological studies have shown that ADD occurs at about the same relative frequency across all social classes and ethnic groups (Lambert et al., 1978; Szatmari et al., 1989). However, conduct disorder and aggressive behavior are more prevalent in low socioeconomic status (SES) groups than in high SES groups. To the degree that minority children are over represented in low SES groups, the presence of associated features of ADD (i.e., conduct disorder and aggressive or defiant behavior) should be proportionally higher.

In educational assessments of minority students, care should be taken to assess ADD and ODD/CD separately, in order to avoid diagnosing ADD on the basis of ODD/CD symptoms. The use of the IOWA or the CLAM rating scales and the independent dimensions of behavior (I/O and A/D) should facilitate this.

The use of some rating scales may overidentify "hyperactive" behavior in minority students. For example, Ullmann et al. (1985) surveyed all second and third grade students in a Midwestern farming and industrial community. The 10 item Conners Teacher Rating Scale was used to obtain subjective ratings for one minority group (the 21.5% of the students were African-American) and a majority group (the 76.4% of the students were Caucasian). In this sample, the average teacher rating was higher for African-American students (M=11.0, SD=6.9) than for Caucasian students (M=8.0, SD=7.0). The recommended cutoff values on this test (a total score of 26 for Caucasian students and 27 for African-American students) identified a greater percentage of African-American students (2.4%) than Caucasian students (1.8%).

When performing an educational assessment of ADD to evaluate a minority student, rating scales which separate inattention from aggression, such as the IOWA or the CLAM, should be used. If available, local norms adjusted for SES should be used. The rating of a referred child should be compared to ratings of students of the same peer group. These precautions may help control for cultural or environmental factors that may lead to biases in subjective ratings of students.

Provisions should be taken in an educational assessment to prevent the misuse of the ADD label for racial or cultural discrimination. Dent (1992) recommended several factors to consider when a minority student is diagnosed with ADD, particularly when the teacher reports ADD symptoms but the parent does not. In some cases, an overt disagreement will be present because the teacher and the parent encounter the same behavior which only the teacher considers to be abnormal. In other cases, an implicit disagreement may exist, because the teacher has encountered ADD symptoms at school which the parent has not noticed in the child's behavior at home.

The following recommendations may help avoid the misuse of the ADD category when the teacher recognizes ADD symptoms but the parent does not:

• Consideration of parent-teacher differences in interpretation or understanding of rating scale items (e.g., *extraneous stimuli, sustaining attention, fidgets*) . If the parent misunderstands items on a rating scale such as the SNAP-IV, then a lack of appreciation of ADD symptoms may occur. Correcting this potential problem may lead to a greater parental acceptance of ADD symptoms offered by the teacher.

• Consideration of situational (home-school) differences in ADD behavior (e.g., inattentive in structured settings at school but not at home). If the parent presents a strong case that the ADD behavior is clearly situational, this may convince the teacher to revise the ADD symptoms based solely on school behavior.

• Consideration of cultural differences in what is considered to be appropriate behavior. Some environments (e.g., inner city schools) may elicit behavior (e.g., decreased compliance; vigorous response to provocation; longer time to initiate response to simple requests) that suggest a diagnosis of ADD. Taken in context, the parent may recognize this pattern of behavior as adaptive and not functionally impairing. If this is true, then the symptoms for ADD diagnosis offered by the teacher should be reconsidered.

This topic has not been addressed adequately in the research literature on ADD. Additional studies are needed to help educators respond in a culturally sensitive way to the new guidelines on the recognition of ADD children.

3.6 Treatment with Stimulants

An educational view is as essential as the medical view of the effects of stimulant medication. A recent attempt to present an educational view (Swanson et al, 1992) will be summarized here. Over 15 years ago, Barkley (1977) and Barkley and Cunningham (1978) pointed out that stimulant medication has little impact on academic achievement of ADD students. Swanson et al. (1991) emphasized that after 15 years of research and clinical experience, there is still no clear evidence that stimulant medication has a long-term effect on school performance. The conclusions of Barkley and Cunningham (1978) still stand: "...the major effect of stimulants appears to be an improvement in classroom manageability rather than academic performance" (p. 85). Based on this conclusion, their recommendation is still sound: stimulant medication should be used as the primary mode of treatment "...only when the goal of treatment is improved manageability" (p. 91).

This educational view of the effects of medication is surprising, because it contrasts sharply with the medical view. For example, Silver (1990) presents a medical view that suggests that about 80% of all ADD children respond favorably to stimulant medications and that when "...these treatment interventions control the behaviors (hyperactivity, distractibility, impulsivity), the child or adolescent can function in the classroom like a nondisabled individual". This medical view is based on strong testimonials about the short-term effects of stimulant medication, which are often dramatic in the eyes of parents and teachers. However, multiple reviews of the literature have been consistent in their conclusions about the limited effect of stimulant medication on learning and academic performance (e.g., Barkley, 1977; Kavale, 1982; Ottenbacher and Cooper, 1983; Swanson et al., 1991).

34

The long-term investigations of ADD children by Satterfield and his colleagues (Satterfield et al., 1979, 1980, 1981, 1987) indicate that stimulant therapy alone has little or no long-term effect on social adjustment or arrest rate during adolescence. In fact, in the long-term follow-up of research cases, Satterfield et al. (1981) reported that only 30% of the ADD children remained on stimulant medication for more than 3 years.

This suggests that the use of stimulant medication in most (but not all) cases is a temporary intervention. Medication may stabilize primary functioning and offer a **window of opportunity** to intervene with nonpharmacological treatments which are intended for permanent application to treat a chronic disorder (Fowler, 1992). Satterfield et al. (1987) have emphasized that medication should not be used to postpone or avoid the more difficult to deliver psychosocial treatments of ADD children and their families.

Treatment of some ADD students with stimulants is absolutely essential. However, careful assessment of the cognitive response is essential to avoid "cognitive toxicity" due to higher than optimal doses (Sprague and Sleator, 1977; Swanson, 1989) or adverse response due impaired learning, social isolation, or dysphoria (Swanson and Kinsbourne, 1978). One way to guard against this is to perform a double-blind assessment of effect of medication on a cognitive measures (acquiring new material or understanding concepts) as well as behavioral measures (compliance or stillness).

Techniques for the cognitive assessment of effects of medication has been presented elsewhere (Swanson and Kinsbourne, 1978; Pelham, 1983; Barkley et al., 1990; Swanson, 1989). Certainly, this approach is not universally accepted (Rapoport et al., 1977), but it does offer a **conservative way to evaluate treatment of ADD with stimulant medication.**

For over 50 years, ADD has been considered a medical problem, and stimulant therapy with medications such as methylphenidate (Ritalin) and d-amphetamine (Dexedrine) has been considered the primary modality of treatment. Reliance on medication may have been unintentionally encouraged by interpretations of the EHA (Bellamy, 1987 and 1989), which disallowed ADD as a handicapping or educationally disabling condition. An unintentionally consequence of this policy may have been to discourage educational interventions as a viable alternative to medication for the treatment of ADD children. The new regulations (Davila et al., 1991) may reverse this and encourage educational intervention as an alternative or complement to medical intervention.

Since this book emphasizes educational aspects of ADD, a detailed review of the strengths and limitations of stimulant medication will not be presented here. Other sources exist which discuss the use of medication in detail (e.g., Wender, 1971; Swanson and Kinsbourne, 1978; Shaywitz and Shaywitz, 1988; Swanson, 1989; Barkley, 1990; Sleator and Pelham, 1990; Silver, 1992).

In the near future, another source specifically for educators will become available based on the products of the US Department of Education's ADD Centers. The extensive literature about the educational impact of stimulant medication on ADD students will be reviewed as part of the ADD Intervention Center at UCI. A literature synthesis on effects of medication will be prepared, and after review and comment at a National Forum in early 1993, this synthesis will be distributed to educators by the US Department of Education.

Pelham (1983) and Gadow (1983) have outlined many methodological weaknesses in the existing research. It is clear that important issues that have not yet been resolved about the long-term effects of stimulant medication on ADD children. The literature suggests but does not prove that stimulants have a limited efficacy for the long-term treatment of ADD.

Research is underway which will address some of the unanswered questions about stimulant therapy. For example, the National Institute of Mental Health (NIMH) Request for Applications (RFA) for the multimodality treatment study of ADD listed the following issues which will be addressed in a 5 year study of medical and psychosocial treatments for ADD:

- No long-term effects have been demonstrated
- In the short-term up to 40% may be non-responders
- High doses may impair learning
- State-dependent learning may occur
- Effects may depend on age and IQ
- Effects may depend on comorbid conditions
- Effects of different stimulants may not be the same
- Attributions of success to pill may offset benefits
- Links to biological factors are not well established
- In most cases length of treatment has been limited

The NIMH-RFA announcement acknowledged "...an important yet limited role for stimulant medication". After medication is used to stabilize primary functioning characteristics, it was speculated that "...behavior and learning problems must then be addressed through a range of psychosocial treatments".

The planned NIMH multimodality treatment study should provide needed information about the long-term effects of the controlled use of stimulant medication to treat ADD students.

37

3.7 Behavioral Treatment

In the most basic form, multimodality treatment includes stimulant therapy and behavior therapy (Pelham, 1989). In educational interventions, this often includes the use of a token reinforcement system in the classroom. Given the amount if time children spend in the classroom, school-based interventions must play an important part of any psychosocial treatment program for ADD children. This book addresses the rationale and techniques for an educational emphasis in multimodality treatment of ADD.

Classroom behavior modification techniques for any school setting can be based on principles of operant conditioning (i.e., reinforcement, punishment, extinction, and stimulus control). These terms in the abstract are difficult to appreciate. In this book, specific examples of applications of these basic principles will be presented and related to educational interventions which have been published in the literature.

Using **reinforcement** will be discussed with reference to the classic study by Masden et al. (1968) on *praise*, and the limitations of this approach will be discussed with reference to the important work of O'Leary et al. (1970) on *token programs*. The use of **punishment** will be discussed with reference to *prudent negatives* (Rosen et al., 1984) and *response cost* (Rapport et al., 1982), as well as *time out* (Barkley, 1990). The use of **extinction** will be discussed with reference to the classic account by Becker (1971) of *ignoring*. The concept of **stimulus control** will be discussed with reference to the work of Marholin and Steinman (1977) and the failure of some effects of token systems to generalize.

An Antecedent-Behavior-Consequence (A-B-C) mnemonic refers to how events in the environment affect behavior. In many source books, a common A-B-C framework is used to discuss the principles of operant conditioning and how they relate to the techniques of behavior modification (e.g., Becker, 1971; Kazdin, 1989). In most applications of behavior modification, an extensive functional analysis is performed to identify the A, B, and C components:

- A: Antecedents (the classroom setting)

- B: Behavior (the student's classroom activities)

- C: Consequences (the events following activities)

For the UCI-CDC programs, the following definitions have been used:

- **A** is defined by the typical classroom period (i.e., a 30-minute to 45-minute period with planned activities to be completed).

- **B** is defined by 5 target classroom activities: getting started, staying on task, interacting with peers, completing work, and stopping and shifting activities.

- **C** is defined by tokens earned as the consequence of appropriate behavior (reinforcement) or lost as the consequences of inappropriate behavior (punishment).

3.8 Established Interventions

As part of the UCI-CDC, a small model school is located on the UCI Campus. This setting is not likely to be duplicated in many places, but over the past 7 years this alternative school for ADD students has provided a place to develop and test intervention models. After the initial development, adaptations are made to facilitate effective application in typical school settings. The successful application of the paraprofessional model in the Irvine Unified School District (see Appendix D) demonstrates the **value of this approach for developing promising practices for school-based interventions with ADD students in regular classroom settings.**

To develop the UCI-CDC multimodality treatment program, it was necessary to overcome resistance based on 2 established views from medicine and education:

• The general **medical practice** of relying primarily on stimulant medication.

• The general **educational practice** of excluding ADD as a handicapping condition.

The staff of the UCI-CDC challenged these prevailing views by emphasizing behavior therapy over medication and by establishing a treatment program in collaboration with the public school system. Discussions of the theoretical basis for multimodality treatment, the empirical basis of each component, and the public school funding of the UCI-CDC school-based intervention program are provided in the articles included as Appendix C and Appendix D of this book.

The most intensive of the UCI-CDC school-based interventions is described in Appendix C. It has 4 components:

> • A classroom behavior modification program.
>
> • A small group training program.
>
> • A medication assessment program.
>
> • A parent training program.

The modification of the UCI-CDC methods and their transfer to the regular classroom setting has been accomplished in the Irvine Unified School District (IUSD). In 1989, 2 of the 4 components were adapted for paraprofessionals to implement in the regular classroom. The UCI-IUSD paraprofessional model is described in Appendix D. It has 2 components:

> • Direct intervention with ADD students in the school setting (i.e., the classroom behavior modification component).
>
> • A pull-out program for skill development (i.e., the small group training component).

In Part III of this book, more details about these educational interventions in the classroom setting will be presented and discussed.

PART II: ASSESSMENT

4. THE SNAP RATING SCALE

4.1 Versions of the SNAP

The items for the initial version of the SNAP rating scale (Swanson, Nolan, and Pelham, 1980) included the 16 DSM-III (1980) symptoms for Attention Deficit Disorder with Hyperactivity (ADD+H). To assess aggressive behavior often associated with ADD (but not part of its definition), 7 Peer Interaction (PI) items were included in this version of the SNAP which measured aggression toward other students. Thus, in its original form, the SNAP rating scale had 23 items -- the 16 DSM-III ADDH items and the 7 PI items.

The DSM-III (1980) symptoms of Oppositional Disorder (OD) and Conduct Disorder (CD) were candidates for items on the original SNAP, but they were not used for the following reasons:

• The DSM-III symptoms for Oppositional Disorder (violation of minor rules; temper tantrums; arguementativeness; provocative behavior; stubborn-ness) were considered to **reflect normal behavior**.

• The DSM-III symptoms for Conduct Disorder (vandalism, rape, breaking and entering, fire-setting, mugging, assault, extortion, purse-snatching, armed robbery, persistent truancy, substance abuse, running away from home, persistent serious lying, stealing) were considered relevant for assessment of adolescents but **not developmentally appropriate** for the assessment of elementary school-aged children.

The SNAP items are taken directly from the DSM symptom lists, so the SNAP rating scale must be revised each time the DSM is revised. Since 1980, 2 revisions of the DSM and the SNAP have been made:

> • In 1987, the SNAP-R was constructed by expanding the original list of 16 ADD items to include the additional and revised items from the DSM-III-R (1987) symptom list for Attention Deficit Hyperactivity Disorder (ADHD), as well as the 9 new items for Oppositional Defiant Disorder (ODD).
>
> • In 1991, the SNAP-IV was constructed by including the items specified in the DSM-IV-WIP (1991) symptom list for ADHD and ADD-H, and by adding the 3 additional items proposed to expand the ODD diagnosis.

Items on the SNAP-IV rating scale represent all of the symptoms for the various formulations of the ADD condition (ADD and ADDH from DSM-III; ADHD and ODD from DSM-III-R; ADHD, ADD-H, and ODD from DSM-IV-WIP). A total of 43 items were required to cover all of the symptoms for these diagnoses.

4.2 Subgroups of ADD Cases

Swanson (1988) recommended the use of the DSM-III-R (1987) diagnosis of ODD along with the diagnosis of ADHD to form 2 subgroups: a nonaggressive subgroup (pure ADD) and an aggressive subgroup (mixed ADD and ODD). This emphasis is based on important distinctions (see Hinshaw, 1987) relevant to behavioral interventions for ADD students in the school setting. Aggressive and non-aggressive ADD students require educators to target different symptoms in school settings for behavior modification programs.

The DSM-III-R subgrouping of ADD based on comorbidity with ODD is different than the DSM-III (1980) subgrouping of ADD based on the presence of Hyperactivity. The DSM-III-R (1987) field tests indicated that the pure ADD (*without* H) cases were rare and that the subgroup of ADD *with H* (ADD+H) accounted for almost all referred cases. However, the literature (Carlson, 1986; Lahey, Hynd, Carlson, and Nieves, 1987) indicates that pure ADD (without H) is an important diagnostic subgroup. These cases often have comorbid internalizing disorders and are less likely to response to stimulant medication (McBurnett, Lahey, and Swanson, 1991).

In DSM-III (1980), 2 subgroups (ADD and ADD+H) were defined by specifically including Hyperactivity symptoms in addition to core symptoms. In DSM-IV-WIP (1991), 2 subgroups (ADHD and ADD-H) were defined by specifically excluding Hyperactivity symptoms from the total set. This new formulation (ADD-H in DSM-IV-WIP) specifies about the same subgroup as the old formulation (ADD in DSM-III), so if the options in DSM-IV-WIP are maintained in the final form of DSM-IV, the "ADD without Hyperactivity" subgroup will reappear as part of the official psychiatric definition.

4.3 SNAP-IV and Multiple Diagnoses

An attractive feature of the SNAP-IV is that summary ratings can be obtained for the various DSM-formulations of ADD and ADHD. However, by including items from all 3 DSM revisions, the SNAP-IV item list became very long. To reduce its length, the 7 Peer Interaction (PI) items were removed from the SNAP-R and were made part of the 16 item CLAM, yielding a 23-item rating scale has been labeled the (S)CLAM (Swanson, Conners, Loney, and Milich) in this book.

The contents of the 3 versions of the SNAP rating scale are summarized below:

• The SNAP (1980) was based on the 16 DSM-III symptoms of ADDH and the 7 PI items.

• The SNAP-R (1987) was based on 43 items, which include all of the DSM-III symptoms; the symptoms added or revised for DSM-III-R for ADHD; 9 ODD symptoms; and the 7 PI items.

• The SNAP-IV (1991) was based on 43 items, which included the DSM-III, DSM-III-R, and DSM-IV-WIP symptoms of ADD and ADHD, the DSM-III-R and DSM-IV-WIP symptoms of ODD, but not the 7 PI items which were shifted to the CLAM rating scale.

The first 22 items on the SNAP-IV are taken from the precise wording of the DSM-IV-WIP (1991) manual. For some DSM-IV-WIP symptoms, minor changes in the DSM-III or DSM-III-R wordings were made (e.g., the addition of the word *Often*). These versions were considered to represent equivalent forms of the symptoms, and only the up-dated versions were listed as SNAP-IV items. DSM-III or DSM-III-R symptoms which were deleted from the DSM-IV-WIP list were included (as items #23 to #31) on the SNAP-IV. Also, the DSM-IV-WIP symptoms of ODD were included (as items #32 to #43) on the SNAP-IV. At the bottom of the SNAP-IV rating form, subcategories of symptoms are listed. The following 9 **item lists** are specified:

> • Four item lists from the DSM-IV-WIP (1991) criteria: Inattention (8 items), Hyperactivity-Impulsivity (10 items), ODD (12 items), and ADD-H (6 of the 8 Inattention items plus 4 additional items).
>
> • Two items lists from the DSM-III-R (1987) criteria: ADHD (14 items) and ODD (9 items).
>
> • Three item lists from DSM-III (1980): Inattention (5 items), Impulsivity (6 items), and Hyperactivity (5 items).

The key at the bottom of the SNAP-IV form provides an easy way to compare the content of the various DSM definitions. Consider the 2 item lists for ADHD. The DSM-IV-WIP (1991) version is based on symptoms of Inattention (#1 to #8) and Hyperactivity-Impulsivity (#9 to #18). The side-by-side lists for DSM-IV-WIP and DSM-III-R on the SNAP-IV key makes it clear that 4 DSM-IV-WIP items -- 2 Inattention items (#6 and #7) and 2 Hyperactivity-Impulsivity items (#10 and #14) -- were added to the DSM-III-R item list.

SNAP-IV RATING SCALE

Name of Child _____ Age _____ Grade _____ Gender _____

Completed by _____ Date _____

Teacher _____ Aide _____ Mother _____ Father _____ Other _____

	Not At All	Just A Little	Pretty Much	Very Much
1. Is often easily distracted by extraneous stimuli	___	___	___	___
2. In absence of close supervision, often has difficulty following through on instructions	___	___	___	___
3. Often has difficulty sustaining attention in tasks or play activities	___	___	___	___
4. Often does not seem to listen to what is being said to him or her	___	___	___	___
5. Often loses things necessary for tasks or activities at school or at home	___	___	___	___
6. Often fails to give close attention to details on schoolwork or other activities	___	___	___	___
7. Often has difficulty organizing goal-directed activities	___	___	___	___
8. Often shifts from one uncompleted activity to another	___	___	___	___
9. Often leaves seat in classroom or in other situations in which remaining seated is expected	___	___	___	___
10. Often acts before thinking	___	___	___	___
11. Often has difficulty awaiting turn in games or group situations	___	___	___	___
12. Often blurts out answers to questions before the questions have been completed	___	___	___	___
13. Often has difficulty playing quietly	___	___	___	___
14. Often runs about or climbs excessively in situations where it is inappropriate	___	___	___	___
15. Often engages in physically dangerous activities without considering possible consequences	___	___	___	___
16. Often fidgets with hands or feet or squirms in seat	___	___	___	___
17. Often interrupts or intrudes on others	___	___	___	___
18. Often talks excessively	___	___	___	___
19. Often stares into space and reports daydreaming	___	___	___	___
20. Often appears to be low in energy level, sluggish, or drowsy	___	___	___	___
21. Is often forgetful in daily activities	___	___	___	___
22. Often appears to be apathetic or unmotivated to engage in goal directed activities	___	___	___	___
23. Often fails to finish things he or she starts	___	___	___	___
24. Has difficulty concentrating on school work or other tasks requiring sustained attention	___	___	___	___
25. Has difficulty sticking to a play activity	___	___	___	___

26. Frequently calls out in class or in other situations when silence is expected _____

27. Has difficulty organizing work (not due to cognitive impairment) _____

28. Needs a lot of supervision _____

29. Moves about excessively (even during sleep) _____

30. Is always "on the go" or acts as if "driven by a motor" _____

31. Often makes careless mistakes in schoolwork or work _____

32. Often loses temper _____

33. Often argues with adults _____

34. Often actively defies or refuses adult requests or rules _____

35. Often deliberately does things that annoy other people _____

36. Often blames others for his or her mistakes or misbehavior _____

37. Often touchy or easily annoyed by others _____

38. Is often angry and resentful _____

39. Is often spiteful or vindictive _____

40. Often swears or uses obscene language _____

41. Often lies _____

42. Often bullies or bosses others _____

43. Often initiates physical fights with other members of his or her household _____

	DSM-IV-WIP (1991)	total	avg
INATT	1_ 2_ 3_ 4_ 5_ 6_ 7_ 8_	__	__
HYP/IMP	9_10_11_12_13_14_15_16_17_18_	__	__
ODD	32_33_34_35_36_37_38_39_40_ 41_42_43_	__	__
ADD-H	2_ 3_ 4_ 5_ 6_ 7_19_20_21_22_	__	__

	DSM-III-R (1987) and [DSM-III] (1980)	total	avg
ADHD	1_ 2_ 3_ 4_ 5_ 8_ 9_11_12_13_15_16_17_18_	__	__
ODD	32_33_34_35_36_37_38_39_40_	__	__
[INATT]	1_ 4_23_24_25_	__	__
[IMP]	8_10_11_26_27_28_	__	__
[HYP]	9_14_16_29_30_	__	__

4.4 Scoring the SNAP

The SNAP approach combined a standard rating scale format and the DSM symptom list, and this combination provided a method to quantify the degree of symptom presence. This quantification allows for the use of a **statistical procedure to determine abnormality** based on the mean (average) and variability (standard deviation) of a comparison group.

Consider the 8 Inattention items from DSM-IV-WIP (1991). An example is presented below to demonstrate the 0 to 3 scoring convention for the 4-point rating scale format:

Rating:	Not At All	Just A Little	Pretty Much	Very Much
Score:	0	1	2	3
• Easily Distracted				✔
• Difficulty Following Through		✔		
• Difficulty Sustaining Attention				✔
• Does Not Seem to Listen				✔
• Loses Necessary Things	✔			
• Fails to Give Close Attention				✔
• Difficulty Organizing Goals			✔	
• Shifts from Activity to Activity				✔
	Total = 20		ARI = 2.5	

As shown in this example, to quantify symptom presence, each item on the SNAP-IV is rated and scored on a 0 to 3 scale: (Not at All = 0, Just A Little = 1, Pretty Much = 2, and Very Much = 3). A subcategory score (in this case, for DSM-IV-WIP Inattention) is obtained by summing items scores and dividing by the number of items in the item list. This yields an **Average Rating Per Item** (ARI) score.

In the example presented, the sum of the item ratings, 3+2+3+3+1+3+2+3 = 20, is interpreted to reflect the degree of symptom presence. This total is divided by the number of items to obtain the ARI score (20/8 = 2.5). This level of severity describes a child whose behavior is rated between *Pretty Much* (which receives a score of 2) and *Very Much* (which receives a score of 3) .

The number of items differ in the DSM-defined disorders and their subcategories (i.e., ADD, ADD+H, ADHD, ADD-H, and ODD). The averaging procedure (**calculating the ARI**) provides a summary score that can be compared across subcategories in a meaningful way even if the subcategories differ in number of items.

It is easier to make meaningful comparisons of ARI scores than of Total scores. For example, consider the DSM-IV-WIP and DSM-III-R version of the ADHD condition. A Total Score of 45 for the DSM-IV-WIP version of ADHD and a Total Score of 35 for the DSM-III-R version of ADHD each yield an ARI score = 2.5. Based on the ARI index, it is clear that these 2 Total Scores (45 and 35) represent equivalent levels of severity (ARI = 2.5) for the 2 versions of the ADHD definition.

In DSM-III (1980), the ADD symptoms of Inattention, Impulsivity, and Hyperactivity were listed separately. The SNAP-IV key shows which items are combined to form the ARI scores for these 3 subcategories of symptoms. The item numbers and ARI calculations are shown below:

category	item numbers	ARI
INATTENTION easily distracted doesn't listen fails to finish difficulty concentrating difficulty sticking to play	1, 4, 23, 24, 25	Total/5
IMPULSIVITY shifts activities excessively acts before thinking frequently calls out in class difficulty awaiting turn difficulty organizing work needs a lot of supervision	8, 10, 11, 26, 27, 28	Total/6
HYPERACTIVITY difficulty staying seated runs about and climbs difficulty sitting still or fidgets moves excessively during sleep on the go, driven by a motor	9, 14, 16, 29, 30	Total/5

4.5 Age and Gender Norms

A statistical procedure can be used to define the **degree of symptom presence** relative to normal childhood behavior. Norms were obtained for the original SNAP (Swanson, 1980), and 2 levels of severity (M+1SD and M+2SD) were proposed based on the mean (average) and standard deviation (variability) of ARI scores, as shown below:

age gender	category (DSM-III)	mean (M)	std dev (SD)	M+1SD (moderate)	M+2SD (severe)
6-7 Boys	INATT	1.29	.95	2.14	3.00
	IMP	1.10	.86	1.96	2.82
	HYP	1.00	.90	1.90	2.80
6-7 Girls	INATT	0.82	.85	1.57	2.42
	IMP	0.63	.79	1.42	2.05
	HYP	0.51	.67	1.18	1.85
8-9 Boys	INATT	0.95	.88	1.83	2.71
	IMP	0.76	.77	1.53	2.30
	HYP	0.81	.79	1.60	2.39
8-9 Girls	INATT	0.54	.78	1.32	2.10
	IMP	0.34	.53	0.87	1.20
	HYP	0.31	.53	0.84	1.37
10-11 Boys	INATT	0.90	.79	1.69	2.48
	IMP	0.68	.71	1.39	2.10
	HYP	0.48	.61	1.09	1.70
10-11 Girls	INATT	0.43	.63	1.06	1.69
	IMP	0.26	.54	0.80	1.30
	HYP	0.27	.41	0.68	1.09

To construct these norms, statistics (M and SD) were calculated to describe the distribution of average rating per item (ARI) scores for a typical population of elementary school students in regular classes. ARI scores were obtained for students based on the 5 Inattention items, the 6 Impulsivity items, and the 5 Hyperactivity items. Separate norms were calculated for boys and girls in three age groups (6-7 years, 8-9 years, and 10-11 years).

If these ARI scores were normally distributed, then statistical principles indicate that the M+1SD cutoff would identify about 17% of the typical student population, and the M+2SD cutoff would identify the top 2% of the students with the most extreme ADD behavior. However, the distributions or scores in the non-referred population are skewed to the right (Ullman et al, 197?), so slightly greater percentages are likely to be identified by the ARI cutoff scores presented with the age and gender norms.

The term *marked degree* in the PGARD educational definition of ADD can be operationalized by the use of a statistical cutoff score. In this book, the M+2SD cutoff score is recommended for use by educators. This should identify approximately 3% to 5% of the elementary school-aged population as having ADD symptoms to a *marked degree*.

By using the same statistical cutoff rule (e.g., M+2SD) for all age and gender groupings, about the **same percentage of girls and boys would be identified** with extreme or abnormal ADD behavior. In the population of girls, the absolute level of ADD reflected by cutoff scores may not be sufficient to produce functional impairment in the classroom. Statistical abnormality based on norms is not sufficient to meet the DSM or PGARD criteria for the definition of ADD: **in all cases, functional impairment is also required.**

The SNAP-IV norms can be used to make 2 important points about teacher ratings of ADD behavior:

> • Mild ADD-like behaviors are characteristics of normal childhood.
>
> • The ratings of ADD-like behaviors of children in regular classrooms vary according to age and gender.

For example, the SNAP norms indicate that the average Inattention Score for 6 to 7 year old boys is 1.29. This indicates that even in non-ADD students, inattention is seen more than *Just A Little* and less than *Pretty Much* in the eyes of the typical teacher. Thus, **the mere presence of ADD symptoms does not indicate abnormality.** The statistical definition proposed here (M+2SD) would require an ARI score near the maximum (3.0) to identify extreme inattention in first grade boys.

As another example, consider the Hyperactivity cutoff score for a 6 to 7 year old girl (M+2SD = 1.85), which is 30% lower than the Hyperactivity cutoff score for a 6 to 7 year old boy (M+2SD = 2.80). The absolute values for teacher ARI scores that reflect *just above average* behavior for boys represent *extreme* behavior for girls.

Based on the ARI information present above, two general recommendations are made. For **young boys** (under 8 years of age), consider an ARI score of 2.5 or greater to be extreme. For **older boys** (over 8 years of age) **and girls** of any age, consider an ARI score of 2.0 to be extreme. In all cases, functional impairment must be confirmed in addition to statistical abnormality to diagnose ADD.

4.6 Symptom Count and the SNAP

ADD behavior should be considered a psychiatric symptom only if it produces functional impairment. Functional impairment exists when the ADD behavior seriously disrupts the student's daily activities in school and has an adverse impact on academic performance. Usually, this level of ADD behavior results in serious adverse consequences, such as school failure, low self esteem, suspension, etc.

Instead of assigning a numerical scores to each item, a rule can be formulated to specify when an item rating represents symptom presence (Pelham et al., 1992). Symptom presence for each item can be operationally defined based on the following assumptions:

• Not At All	=	Not Present
• Just a Little	=	Present but Not Bothersome
• Pretty Much	=	Bothersome but Not Impairing
• Very Much	=	Impairing

Pelham et al. (1992) reported prevalence estimates of ADD in elementary school-aged boys (5 to 14 years old) based on a symptom count approach. The *Very Much* criterion for symptom presence applied in conjunction with the DSM-III-R criterion of 8 or more of the 14 ADHD symptoms for a diagnosis of ADHD. Using these criteria, about 6% of the school-aged population of boys was identified as having ADD. (If it is assumed that girls would have a prevalence only 1/3 as high as boys, these data suggest an overall prevalence of about 4%.)

4.7 The Bloomingdale Criteria

The Bloomingdale-ADD criteria (Swanson, Shea, McBurnett, Potkin, Fiore, and Crinella, 1990) are based on a symptom count approach that is more stringent than the recommendations of DSM-III (1980) or DSM-III-R (1987). Based on the Research Diagnostic Criteria derived from the Fifth Bloomingdale Symposium (Sergeant, 1988), a symptom list of 8 items was proposed, and a stringent symptom count criterion (6 out of 8 or 75% of the listed symptoms) was recommended for a diagnosis of ADD.

The DSM-III list has 16 items, and 8 out of the 16 (50%) are required for a diagnosis of ADDH. Based on the subcategory requirements, 6 out of 11 (55%) are required for a diagnosis of ADD. The DSM-III-R list has 14 items, and 8 out of 14 (57%) are required for a diagnosis of ADHD. The DSM-IV-WIP list has 18 items, but the number of symptoms required for a diagnosis of ADD or ADHD has not yet been set.

Swanson et al. (1990) suggested that the Bloomingdale-ADD criteria were more stringent than the DSM-III or the DSM-III-R criteria **because a higher percentage of listed symptoms was required for a diagnosis of ADD**. A more stringent symptom count criterion would result in a lower prevalence of identified ADD cases. By setting the symptom count criterion at 75% of listed symptoms, it is likely that 3% or less of the school-aged population would receive a diagnosis of ADD.

A lenient criterion for identification of ADD students might overwhelm an already over-taxed special education system. The use of the Bloomingdale-ADD criteria should identify the most severe cases and set the prevalence of ADD at a manageable level from the perspective of educators who must use scarce resources to serve students from many categories.

5. THE CLAM RATING SCALE

5.1 The IOWA Rating Scale

Conners (1969) developed a rating scale to evaluate the condition commonly called just **hyperactivity** before the criteria for ADD and ADDH were proposed in DSM-III (1980). A 10-item subset of a 39-item Conners Teacher Rating Scale was selected to form an index score. In the 1970s, this 10-item list (the Abbreviated Conners Rating Scale) became the standard for diagnosing hyperactivity.

Loney and Milich (1982) noted that some items of the Abbreviated Conners Rating Scale were associated with 2 components of behavior: inattention/overactivity (I/O) and aggression/defiance (A/D). These mixed items were not specific for ADD behavior since high ratings on them could reflect either high levels of I/O behavior (ADD symptoms) or high levels of A/D behavior (ODD/CD symptoms). To make ratings specific for these 2 dimensions of behavior, Loney and Milich (1982) developed the Inattention and Overactivity with Aggression (IOWA) rating scale. The IOWA-Conners rating scale was constructed using **divergent validity** techniques. Starting with the items from the Conners Teacher Rating Scale, 2 sets of items were selected:

> • a pure I/O set of 5 items which measured the component of hyperactive behavior that was independent of aggression/defiance (A/D).
>
> • a pure A/D set of 5 items which measured the component of hyperactive behavior that was independent of inattention/overactivity (I/O).

The 5 pure I/O items selected by the divergent validity procedures are presented below:

- Fidgeting
- Makes odd noises
- Excitable, impulsive
- Inattentive, distractible
- Fails to finish, short attention span

The 5 pure A/D items are the following:

- Quarrelsome
- Acts smart
- Temper outbursts
- Defiant
- Uncooperative

It is important to note that this divergent validity procedure removed some of the items which were the most frequently reported referral symptoms, including the following 5 items:

- Restless or overactive
- Disturbs other children
- Mood changes quickly and drastically
- Demands must be met immediately
- Teases others, interferes with activities

Swanson (1988) expanded the 10-item IOWA by including the 5 mixed items identified by Loney and Milich (1982) as well as a single item (*Cries often and easily*) to complete the set of items of the Abbreviated Conners Teacher Rating Scale. The resulting 16-item rating scale was called the CLAM. In this book, the 7 PI items from the SNAP were added to the 16-item CLAM to form the 23-item SCLAM rating scale.

59

(SKCLAM RATING SCALE

Name of Child _____ Age _____ Grade _____ Gender _____
Completed by _____ Date _____
Teacher _____ Aide _____ Mother _____ Father _____ Other _____

Check each column which
best describes this child:

	Not At All	Just A Little	Pretty Much	Very Much
1. Fidgeting				
2. Hums and makes other odd noises				
3. Excitable, impulsive				
4. Inattentive, easily distracted				
5. Fails to finish things he or she starts (short attention span)				
6. Quarrelsome				
7. Acts "smart"				
8. Temper outbursts (explosive and unpredictable behavior)				
9. Defiant				
10. Uncooperative				
11. Restless or overactive				
12. Disturbs other children				
13. Mood changes quickly and drastically				
14. Demands must be met immediately (easily frustrated)				
15. Teases other children and interferes with their activities				
16. Cries often and easily				

17. Fights, hits, or punches ⎯⎯
18. Is disliked by other children ⎯⎯
19. Frequently interrupts other childrens activities ⎯⎯
20. Bossy; always telling other children what to do ⎯⎯
21. Teases or calls other children names ⎯⎯
22. Refuses to participate in group activities ⎯⎯
23. Often loses temper ⎯⎯

In your own words, describe three noteworthy (favorable or unfavorable) events which occurred during this rating period.
If there were no noteworthy events, describe three things which happened even if they were unremarkable.

1. _____

2. _____

3. _____

		total	avg
PURE I/O	1_ 2_ 3_ 4_ 5_	⎯	⎯
PURE A/D	6_ 7_ 8_ 9_10_	⎯	⎯
MIXED I/O+A/D	11_12_13_14_15_	⎯	⎯
CONNERS INDEX	1_ 3_ 4_ 5_ 8_11_12_13_14_16_	⎯	⎯
SNAP-PI	17_18_19_20_21_22_23_		

61

5.2 Cutoff Scores

The SCLAM ratings can be use to calculate average rating per item (ARI) scores for 5 sets of items: pure I/O, pure A/D, mixed I/O+A/D, the Conners Index, and the PI. The CLAM items numbers for these 5 subsets are shown below:

dimension	item numbers	# of items
PURE I/O	1, 2, 3, 4, 5	5 items
PURE A/D	6, 7, 8, 9,10	5 items
MIXED I/O+A/D	11,12,13,14,15	5 items
CONNERS	1, 3, 4, 5, 8,	10 items
(10 item index)	11,12,13,14,16	
SNAP-PI	17,18,19,20,21,	7 items
(peer interaction)	22,23	

To establish norms for the IOWA, Loney and Milich (1982) evaluated elementary school aged boys in regular classroom settings. Based on these norms they recommended cutoffs based on **total scores** (i.e., the sum of 5 item ratings). For the I/O dimension, the M+1SD cutoff (Over 7) identified about 20% of the school-aged population. The M+2SD cutoff (Over 11) identified about 5%. For the A/D dimension, the M+1SD cutoff (Over 4) identified about 20% of the population, and the M+2SD cutoff (Over 7) identified about 5%.

The cutoff based on Total scores can be transformed to ARI scores by dividing by 5. When this is done, the equivalent ARI scores for the I/O dimension are 1.4 (M+1SD) and 2.2 (M+2SD). For the A/D cutoffs, the equivalent ARI scores are .8 (M+1SD) and 1.4 (M+2SD).

ARI scores for the SCLAM were calculated from the Milich and Pelham (1988) norms for Inattention/Overactivity (I/O) and Aggression/Defiance (A/D) and the Swanson et al. (1980) norms for Peer Interaction (PI). In the table below, ARI scores for I/O, A/D, and PI are presented for age and gender subgroups:

Age Gender	Dimension	Mean	SD	M+1SD	M+2SD
6-7 Boys	I/O	0.96	.83	1.79	2.62
	A/D	0.55	.73	1.28	2.01
	PI	0.75	.75	1.50	2.25
6-7 Girls	I/O	0.54	.62	1.16	1.78
	A/D	0.43	.69	1.12	1.81
	PI	0.55	.69	1.24	1.93
8-9 Boys	I/O	0.76	.86	1.62	2.48
	A/D	0.55	.82	1.37	2.19
	PI	0.60	.60	1.20	1.80
8-9 Girls	I/O	0.39	.67	1.06	1.73
	A/D	0.17	.37	0.54	0.91
	PI	0.28	.50	0.78	1.28
10-11 Boys	I/O	0.45	.73	1.18	1.91
	A/D	0.36	.60	0.96	1.56
	PI	0.42	.54	0.96	1.50
10-11 Girls	I/O	0.38	.56	0.94	1.50
	A/D	0.20	.46	0.66	1.12
	PI	0.28	.53	0.81	1.34

5.3 Pure and Mixed Subtypes

Loney and Milich (1982) compared individuals' I/O and A/D scores on the IOWA rating scale to statistical cutoffs recommended for clinical (M+1SD) and research (M+2SD) purposes. Based on the cutoffs on the 2 dimensions of behavior, Loney and Milich (1982) identified 4 subtypes:

- Exclusively Hyperactive (over cutoff on I/O only)

- Aggressive Only (over cutoff on the A/D only)

- Hyperactive and Aggressive (over cutoffs on both)

- Neither Hyperactive or Aggressive (below cutoffs)

Even though all 4 subgroups are possible, most children referred for an assessment of ADD will have high I/O scores, thus eliminating 2 of the 4 subgroups. For that reason, an individual's A/D score provides the most important information for determining subgroup placement. The percentages for subgroups derived from the SCLAM are presented below:

- pure I/O (about 25% of referred cases)

- pure A/D (less than 10% of referred cases)

- mixed I/O&A/D (about 50% of referred cases)

- neither I/O nor A/D (about 15% of referred cases)

6. THE SKAMP RATING SCALE

6.1 Classroom Target Behaviors

The Swanson, Kotkin, Agler, M-Flynn, and Pelham (SKAMP) rating scale was developed to evaluate the target behaviors specified in UCI-CDC school-based behavior modification program. In the ADD literature on behavior modification, the following set of 5 target behaviors has been specified (see Pelham, 1989; Swanson, 1988; Swanson et al., 1990):

- getting started on classroom assignments
- staying on task for a classroom period
- interacting with peers in the classroom
- completing work on the classroom assignment
- shifting activities with the class

The SKAMP rating scale was formed by adding items describing 5 other important classroom behaviors which have been specified for the UCI-CDC intervention programs:

- remaining quiet when required by class rules
- remaining seated when required by class rules
- interacting with staff (teacher or aide)
- performing written work accurately and neatly
- directing effort to class activities

The item selection for the SKAMP was based on the observation that ADD students have 2 types of problems: **Attention** problems which lead to decreased academic productivity, and **Deportment** problems which lead to classroom disruptions.

Based on the SNAP-IV conventions, each item of the SKAMP is rated on a four point scale and a numerical score is assigned (i.e., *Not At All* = 0; *Just A Little* = 1; *Pretty Much* = 2; *Very Much* = 3). The items ratings on the SKAMP are combined in subsets to reflect attention and deportment in the classroom:

SKAMP ITEM	ITEM NUMBER
• Orienting Attention 　getting started 　stopping and switching	1, 10
• Maintaining Attention 　staying on task 　completing work	2, 7
• Directing Attention 　accurate and neat 　attending to activities	8, 9
Total Attention	1, 2, 7, 8, 9, 10
• Attention to Others 　interaction with peers 　interactions with staff	3, 4
• Attention to Rules 　remaining quiet 　remaining seated	5, 6
Total Deportment	3, 4, 5, 6

The SKAMP is a new rating scale and has not yet been evaluated by statistical procedures (e.g., factor analysis). Thus, at this time these 2 subgroups of symptoms (attention and deportment) are based solely on experiences in the classroom and concepts behind the intervention programs.

SKAMP RATING SCALE

Name of Child _____ Age _____ Grade _____ Gender _____
Completed by _____ Date _____
Teacher _____ Aide _____ Mother _____ Father _____ Other _____

Check each column which
best describes this child
during a classroom period:

	Not At All	Just A Litle	Pretty Much	Very Much
1. Difficulty getting started on classroom assignments	___	___	___	___
2. Difficulty staying on task for a classroom period	___	___	___	___
3. Problems in interactions with peers in the classroom	___	___	___	___
4. Problems in interactions with staff (teacher or aide)	___	___	___	___
5. Difficulty remaining quiet according to classroom rules	___	___	___	___
6. Difficulty staying seated according to classroom rules	___	___	___	___
7. Problems in completion of work on classroom assignments	___	___	___	___
8. Problems in accuracy or neatness of written work in the classroom	___	___	___	___
9. Difficulty attending to an activity or discussion of the class	___	___	___	___
10. Difficulty stopping and making transition to next period	___	___	___	___

		total	avg
ATTENTION			
Orienting Attention	1_10_	___	___
Maintaining Attention	2_ 7_	___	___
Directing Attention	8_ 9_	___	___
Total Attention	1_ 2_ 7_ 8_ 9_10_	___	___

		total	avg
DEPORTMENT			
Attention to Others	3_ 4_	___	___
Attention to Rules	5_ 6_	___	___
Total Deportment	3_ 4_ 5_ 6_	___	___

6.2 Norms for the SKAMP

Limited SKAMP norms are available for 10 year old elementary school children. The average rating per item (ARI) scores are presented below:

Subgroup	Mean	SD	M+1SD	M+2SD
BOYS				
Attention	.84	1.01	1.85	2.86
Deportment	.82	.82	1.64	2.46
GIRLS				
Attention	.41	.73	1.14	1.87
Deportment	.37	.55	.92	1.47

These SKAMP norms can be used to specify **the severity of ADD in the classroom**. Age adjustments can be made for assessing students younger than 10 years of age (by requiring higher cutoff scores) or older than 10 year of age (by requiring lower cutoff scores).

6.3 SKAMP Link to Intervention

The SKAMP offers an advantage over the SNAP-IV rating scale. Each of the items of the SKAMP was designed to be the *B* in an Antecedent-Behavior-Consequence (A-B-C) analysis of behavior. This provides a link between assessment and treatment of the educational manifestations of ADD.

In the A-B-C analysis of ADD behavior, the **Antecedent** conditions are specified as the class period. Each SKAMP item SKAMP item represents a **Behavior** associated with attention and deportment in the classroom. **Consequences** can be specified in a simple token reinforcement program. Multiple sources in literature (e.g., Becker, 1971; O'Leary and O'Leary, 1977; Walker and Buckley, 1972; Kazdin, 1989; Pelham, 1989) clearly show that token reinforcement programs can be implemented based on the principles of operant conditioning (i.e., reinforcement and punishment). Intervention strategies based on reinforcement (positive consequences such as praise and points earned for appropriate attention and deportment in the classroom) can be used to **increase** academic productivity. Strategies based on punishment (such as *response cost* or *time out* for inappropriate attention or deportment in the classroom) can be used to **decrease** noncompliance with rules and disruptive interactions in the class.

The SKAMP was written to match the SNAP-IV rating scale in order to assess deficits (Inappropriate Behaviors) associated with ADD. The behavioral opposites (Appropriate Behaviors) are stated as targets in the UCI-CDC behavior modification programs, in order to intervene with Reinforcement rather than Punishment strategies. This difference in the definition of Behaviors for purposes of assessment and intervention will be discussed in Part III of this book.

7. DIRECT OBSERVATIONS

7.1 Classroom Observations

A Classroom Observation of Conduct and Attention Disorders (COCADD) procedure has been used to verify the differences in classroom behavior of students with **hyperactivity** and **aggression**. This work has been published in a series of papers by Atkins, Pelham, and Licht (1985, 1988 and 1989).

In this research program, the SNAP and IOWA rating scales were used to define ADD and CD. Instead of using the OD items (e.g., stubborn, provocative, etc.) or CD items (e.g. vandalism, rape, etc.), this research group defined CD based on the 7 SNAP peer interaction (PI) items. These items describe overt behaviors associated with the core CD symptoms of **aggression** (fights; bossy; teases; loses temper), **social incompetence** (disliked by peers; interrupts; refuses to participate in group activities) and **defiance** (quarrelsome; acts smart; temper outbursts; defiant; uncooperative).

Atkins, Pelham, and Licht (1985) used 3 types of assessments to make direct observations of classroom behaviors: a classroom behavioral observation method (COCADD), a systematic review of classroom academic output (class assignments completed correctly), and checks of student readiness based on materials on hand (desk observations).

The COCADD uses brief (2-sec) but frequent observations in the classroom and on the playground. Composite measures (e.g., Attending, Verbal Off-Task, etc.) are derived from individual behavioral codes (e.g., sitting, talking to self, etc.).

Based on observations of classroom and playground behavior, and direct inspection of the child's environment (the desk) and school work, 23 measures in 4 areas were defined:

- The **classroom observations** yielded 8 measures (Attending, Distracted, Verbal Off-Task, Verbal Disruptive, Stealing/Cheating, Verbal Aggressive, Physical Aggressive, and Overactive).

- The **playground observations** yielded 8 measures (Verbal Disruptive, Stealing/Cheating, Verbal Aggressive, Physical Aggressive, High Active Play, Solitary Play, Parallel Play, Group Play).

- The **desk observations** yielded 5 measures (Neat Desktop, Neat Inside Desk, Neat Desk Area, Has Books, Has Materials).

- The **academic observations** yielded 2 measures (Assignments Completed and % Correct).

This research of Atkins, Pelham, and Licht (1985, 1988, 1991) related subjective teacher ratings of ADD symptoms (from the SNAP) to actual behavioral acts and academic products from the school setting. This work provided empirical support for the use of the SNAP and IOWA teacher rating scales.

7.2 Observations and Diagnosis

Atkins, Pelham, and Licht (1985) verified that the SNAP ratings of ADD symptoms has the expected association with direct observations (*Assignments Completed, Distracted*) and preparation for work (*Has a Pencil*). This research also documented that 3 direct observations (*Attending, Verbal Intrusion, and %Correct*), which were important for distinguishing ADD from non-ADD students. The direct observation items match the content of the DSM-III (1980) core symptoms of inattention and impulsivity.

Atkins, Pelham, and Licht (1989) evaluated the validity of IOWA rating scale. Teacher ratings of I/O and A/D from the IOWA rating scale were correlated with the observation measures (described above) revealed that three measures of academic productivity and readiness (*%Correct, Number of Assignments Completed, and Neat Desktop*) yielded different correlations with I/O and A/D.

Based on this research program, Atkins, Pelham, and Licht (1991) recommended the following empirically derived set of items to differentiate ADD students from non-ADD students:

- Verbal intrusion in the classroom
- Talking to self in the classroom
- Not sitting in the classroom
- Low percentage correct on written assignments
- Not prepared to work (no pencil or eraser)

In the statistical analyses of the assessments of ADD students, this set of observations provided a **sensitive** test (i.e., 76% correct identification of ADD cases) and a **specific** test (i.e., 91% correct for identification of non-ADD cases).

7.3 The Restricted Academic Setting

In the evaluation of ADD children, IQ and achievement tests are often administered. One of the valuable products of testing is the description by the examiner of the student's on-task behavior. A systematic procedure for evaluating the percentage of time on-task in an analog academic setting was developed by Roberts, Milich, and Loney (1984) and Roberts (1990). Simple analogue academic tasks were developed from standard coding and cancellation tasks.

The material for a **coding task** can be prepared by printing paired symbols (e.g., letters and digits) on the top line of a page, followed by about 10 rows of multiple letters (e.g., 15 to 20 per row). A small empty box or blank line is placed underneath each letter. The material for the **cancellation task** can be prepared by printing a single character (a letter or a digit) at the top of a page, followed by about 20 rows of multiple characters (letters or digits). For each of these test, several pages should be prepared, with a new definition of the target letter at the top of each page. The task are alternated, with a specific time allowed (3 minutes) before going to the next task.

Performance measures (*# coded and # cancelled*) are taken from the permanent products (i.e., the marked sheets of paper) of the tests. However, the most important data are derived from observations made at regular intervals (every 5 seconds) during the testing to estimate the percentage of allotted time spent on the task (*% on task*).

The instruction for the cancellation task are simple. For the example given below, the student is told to *Mark out all of the 5's that you see:*

5

2	3	7	8	1	2	3	5	3	5	3
6	2	9	1	4	5	8	9	2	3	7
5	3	0	2	9	3	2	5	0	1	8
9	1	9	3	6	8	5	1	9	0	7
4	8	2	7	5	1	8	9	6	3	2

The instruction for the coding task are simple. For the example given below, the student is told to *fill in each blank with the correct number*:

W	T	F	A	V	E	N	Y	S	C
1	2	3	4	5	6	7	8	9	0

C V T S E W Y T W F A C W A

___ ___ ___ ___ ___ ___ ___ ___ ___ ___ ___ ___ ___ ___

A T W N A Y T A F W V S E N

___ ___ ___ ___ ___ ___ ___ ___ ___ ___ ___ ___ ___ ___

7.4 Attention and Performance Measures

Performance measures on the cancellation and coding tests are scored by counting how many items are completed correctly or incorrectly over the 15 minute period. It is important to note that a performance score will be related to ability, and therefore may not be a good measure of attention. Thus, the Number Correct scores on the coding and cancellations tests are not the critical measures. Instead, the critical measure is the *%On-Task* score. This type of measurement of behavior represents the student's **attention directed to the task** rather than the student's performance on the test. On these tests, performance measures (i.e., number of pairs coded or number of digits detected or missed) are likely to be related to IQ.

The *%On-Task* is a measure of the behavior associated with attention. In the Roberts et al. (1984) protocol, the *%On-Task* score is based on the on-task and off-task coding **every 5-seconds** for the intervals derived from three 5-minute observation periods. A simple calculation is used:

$$\%On\text{-}Task = (\#On\text{-}Task) / (\#On\text{-}Task + \#Off\text{-}Task)$$

Roberts (1990) reported that these **simple, easily administered tasks to be effective for the identification of ADD students.** The ADD students were observed to be on-task less than 50% of the time, while the non-ADD students were observed to be on-task about 90% of the time. An 80% cutoff value for the *%On-Task* score correctly identified about 85% of the ADD students and about 95% of the non-ADD students.

7.5 The TOVA and GDS

Two commercial tests have been marketed as diagnostic tests for ADD: the Test of Variables of Attention (TOVA) and the Gordon Diagnostic System (GDS).

Both the TOVA (Greenberg, 1991) and the GDS (Gordon, 1983) are based on the Continuous Performance Test (CPT). The CPT is designed to be extremely boring. It requires the child to perform a repetitive activity (waiting for specific letter or geometric shape to appear on a computer screen) in a sequence of presentations that lasts for 10 to 20 minutes. The CPT measures a specific aspect of sustained attention (the ability to attend and respond to a stimulus in a boring, repetitive activity). In some respects, the CPT is similar to the coding and cancellation tests, except that the CPT is not intended to be an analogue academic test.

The CPT not a specific test for ADD because poor performance on it is characteristic of children with many disorders other than ADD. In fact, CPT tests were developed to measure the inattention in individuals with psychiatric disorders such as schizophrenia, not ADD! Poor performance on the CPT does not diagnose ADD. The standard ratings and interviews, with an emphasis on exclusion as well as inclusion criteria, are still essential if a CPT test is administered.

The TOVA or the GDS should not be used as the sole (or even the primary) source of information for a diagnosis of ADD. This is emphasized in the TOVA manual: "the TOVA and other CPTs do not diagnose attention deficit disorders" and should be used only "as part of a multi-faceted, multi-disci-plinary assessment" (Greenberg, 1991). The CPT test merely provides a direct measure of performance which can be used to provide a snapshot of behavior to confirm or refute a diagnosis based on specific and chronic symptoms of ADD.

7.6 IQ and Achievement Tests

The PGARD educational definition of ADD expressed the consensus opinion that low achievement test performance, low IQ, or a discrepancy between IQ and achievement are not diagnostic signs of ADD.

Achievement tests and IQ tests are recommended to check for exclusion conditions, such as an unrecognized learning disability reflected by an IQ-achievement discrepancy) or low level of intellectual ability. If either of these conditions exists but is unrecognized, then ADD-like symptoms may be the result of inappropriate placement and expectations.

A particular pattern of performance on the Wechsler Intelligence Scale for Children-Revised (WISC-R) -- relatively low scores on the coding, arithmetic, and digit span subtests -- may be associated with ADD. This triad of subtest scores has been used to form a third IQ factor (in addition to the Verbal and Performance factors) called "freedom from distractibility" (FFD). Many ADD children do have low FFD scores, but the educational literature has identified a problem in applying this to diagnose ADD: low WISC-FFD scores may also characterize children with other non-ADD conditions (e.g., learning disabilities). Some support may be derived for the use of the FFD from a report by Forness et al (1991). In a group of ADD children without learning disabilities, the FFD subtests averaged about 1 SD below the mean (M=8.9, SD=2.5) of the other clusters of subtests (e.g., Verbal and Perceptual) of the WISC-R (M=11.2, SD=2.3). The diagnostic significance of this finding has not been established and must await replication. The use of the FFD measure from the WISC-R will be complicated in future studies by a recent change in subtests included in the FFD factor on the revised WISC-III (1992).

PART III: INTERVENTION

8. EDUCATIONAL INTERVENTIONS

8.1 Multimodality Treatment

As discussed in Part I of this book, stimulant medication is the most common treatment for ADD, but clinical use and research have not produced evidence of long-term effects on social adjustment or academic achievement (Barkley, 1977; Barkley and Cunningham, 1978). In an article in a recent special series on ADD in the *Journal of Learning Disabilities*, Swanson, Cantwell, Lerner, McBurnett, and Hanna (1991) presented a detailed review of these issues, and in an article for educators in *Beyond Behavior,* Swanson, Cantwell, Lerner, McBurnett, Pfiffner, and Kotkin (1992) emphasized the limitations of stimulant therapy.

Since stimulant therapy alone has not been demonstrated to be an effective long term treatment for ADD, many clinicians and investigators have suggested that multimodality treatment of ADD is necessary (e.g., Satterfield et al., 1987; Pelham, 1989; Swanson et al., 1990; NIMH-RFA, 1992). **In its most basic form, multimodality treatment consists of the combination of behavior therapy and stimulant therapy.** It is essential to understand both of these components to deliver effective multimodality treatment.

As outlined in Part I, many sources (e.g., books and articles) exist which offer explanations and discussions of stimulant therapy, so detailed information about this medical component will not be presented here. Instead, this book will present background information about behavior therapy, and the emphasis will be on how behavior therapy has been applied in the educational setting of the UCI-CDC multimodality treatment programs for ADD students.

8.2 Technical Terms

Behavior modification techniques are based on the principles of operant conditioning. As in any specialized area, technical terms or *jargon* are necessary for discussion. A brief review will be presented of several terms which are necessary to describe the UCI-CDC applications of behavior therapy.

In an excellent book on behavior modification, Kazdin (1989) summarized 4 basic principles of operant conditioning:

• **Reinforcement** occurs when presenting an event increases the likelihood of behavior it follows.

• **Punishment** occurs when presenting an event decreases the likelihood of behavior it follows.

• **Extinction** occurs when withholding reinforcement decreases the likelihood of behavior it follows.

• **Stimulus Control** occurs when presenting reinforcement (after behavior occurring in the presence of one stimulus but not another) increases the likelihood of the behavior in the presence of the first stimulus and decreases the likelihood of the behavior in the presence of the other.

These principles of operant conditioning will be discussed in some detail here, since they provide the basis for the development of behavior modification techniques which have been adapted for school-based applications in the UCI-CDC multimodality treatment programs for ADD students.

In Part I of this book, the A-B-C mnemonic was discussed. For an A-B-C analysis, *Behavior* is defined as an event that can be observed and counted. The event that precedes a specific behavior of an individual is called the *Antecedent*. The event that follows a specific behavior of an individual is called a *Consequence*. As outlined by Kazdin (1989), these terms define the A-B-C framework for describing "...the relationship between behavior and the environmental events (antecedents and consequences) that influence behavior" (p. 26). The A-B-C framework is summarized below:

- **Antecedents** precede the behaviors of an individual.

- **Behaviors** are observable activities of an individual.

- **Consequences** follow the behaviors of an individual.

To explain how operant conditioning shapes behavior, Skinner (1987) described **selection by consequences**. When a Behavior is consistently followed by a Reinforcing Consequence, that Behavior is more likely to occur when the Antecedent occurs again. When a Behavior is consistently followed by a Punishing Consequence, that Behavior is less likely to occur when that Antecedent occurs again.

In this way, environmental events (Consequences) select the Behaviors of an individual which are likely to occur in specific contexts (Antecedents).

An empirical process is used to define whether a new Consequence is a Reinforcement or a Punishment. Multiple observations in specific Antecedent conditions are required to determine if the new Consequence results in a long-term change in Behavior. If these observations show that the Behavior becomes more likely, then the Consequence is defined as a Reinforcement. If the Behavior becomes less likely, then the Consequence is defined as a Punishment.

It is important to note that the long-term effect of consequences on behavioral tendencies, not the immediate effects following a particular instance, must be used in this empirical process. The intent of an individual arranging a Consequence does not define whether it is a Reinforcement or a Punishment. According to the principles of operant conditioning, only the change in Behavior of the individual over time is used to define (in technical terms) whether a Consequence is a Reinforcement or a Punishment. Examples from the literature will be used to demonstrate the application of this empirical process to define Reinforcing Consequences and Punishing Consequences.

The literature on behavior therapy provides many examples of how the principles of operant conditioning have been applied as behavior modification techniques. In the usual behavior modification program, arranging consistent Consequences provides the primary technique to change Behavior. Examples will be presented in the next section which demonstrate how the 4 basic principles (reinforcement, punishment, extinction, and stimulus control) have been applied in educational interventions with children.

8.3 Examples of Reinforcement

Several classic studies of Reinforcement in the classroom setting will be presented in this section. These early studies were conducted in the 1960's and 1970's, so they predated the modern definition of ADD (DSM-III, 1980). However, the children investigated in these studies manifested many of the characteristics of what now is known as ADD.

Masden, Becker, and Thomas (1968) published a classic study of **Reinforcement** based on the concept of "catching the child being good". The simple instructions to teachers in this study (p. 145) included the following statements:

> • "Teachers are inclined to take good behavior for granted and pay attention when a child acts up or misbehaves. We are now asking you to try something different."
>
> • "This procedure is characterized as 'catching the child being good' and making a comment designed to reward the child for good behavior. Give praise, attention, or smile when the child is doing what is expected during the particular class period in question."
>
> • "Pay close attention to those children who normally engage in a great deal of misbehavior. Watch carefully and when the child begins to behave appropriately, make a comment such as, you're doing a fine job."
>
> • "At first you will probably get the feeling that you are praising a great deal and it sounds a little phony to your ears. This is a typical reaction and it becomes more natural with he passage of time".

Teachers were also advised to use physical signs of approval (a pat or a touch on the back; an approving facial expression; smiles) in combination with quiet verbal praise delivered so that it does not interfere with ongoing class activities.

The children selected for this study had a history of ADD-like behavior in the classroom, including "fiddling with objects", "talking", "doing nothing", "bothering others", "not hearing directions", and "not engaging in constructive work".

Three conditions were established. The first condition ("Rules") was based on the hypothesis that "...telling children what is expected of them should have considerable effect on their behavior" (p. 143). Five or 6 simple rules were written on the chalkboard and were reviewed frequently (5.2 times per day). The second condition ("Ignoring") was based on the hypothesis that "...attention to Inappropriate Behavior may serve to strengthen the very behavior that the attention is intended to diminish" (p. 144). The third condition ("Praise") was based on the hypothesis that "...persistence in catching children being good and delivering praise and attention should eventually pay off in a better behaved classroom" (p. 145).

Examples of attention to Inappropriate Behavior included:

- "You know you are supposed to be working."

- "Will you stop bothering your neighbors?"

- "Can you keep your hands off!"

- "Stop running around and do your work."

- "Please stop rocking your chair."

The teachers in this study were specifically instructed to **catch students being good** by praising them "...for concentrating on individual work, responding to questions, paying attention to directions and following through, sitting in desk and studying, and sitting quietly if noise has been a problem" (p. 145).

The following examples of simple praise were given during the training of the teachers who participated in this study:

* "I like the way you're doing your work quietly."

* "That's the way I like to see you work!"

* "That's a very good job."

* "You are doing fine."

* "You got two right, that's very good!"

To document the impact of 3 experimental conditions (Rules, Ignoring, and Praise), the classroom behaviors of teachers and the classroom behaviors of students were recorded systematically (using defined classes of behaviors and a 10 second observation interval) for 20 minutes per day.

First consider teacher behavior. The first condition (Rules) did not have an effect on teacher behavior, the second condition (Ignoring) had a small impact on teacher behavior, but the third condition (Praise) dramatically affected teacher behavior. Teachers were able to follow the instructions of the Praise condition, and as a result positive interactions (*Approval of Appropriate Behavior* and *Academic Recognition*) were observed to increase and negative interactions (*Disapproval of Behavior* and *Time Out*) with students were observed to decrease in the classroom.

Based on systematic observation of the selected disruptive students in the classroom, a high rate of inappropriate student behavior (occurring in 50% to 80% of the observation intervals) was documented before intervention. This high rate of inappropriate behavior continued when the first two conditions (Rules and Ignoring) were implemented. When the third condition (Praise) was implemented, the high rate of inappropriate student behavior decreased dramatically (occurring in only 20% of the observation intervals).

The A-B-C analysis introduced earlier in this book can be used to evaluate changes in the Antecedents and Consequences in this study. The following conclusions are warranted:

• Changing the Antecedents by stating Rules did **not** significantly change the target Behaviors (of the students or the teacher) being observed in the classroom.

• Changing the Consequences by increasing Ignoring did **not** produce a significant change in the targeted Behaviors (Inappropriate Behavior in the Classroom). In term of the principles of operant conditioning, Extinction did not operate, suggesting that negative attention was not a Reinforcing Consequence as hypothesized.

• Changing the Consequences by increasing Praise **did** produce a change in the targeted Behaviors (Appropriate Behavior in the Classroom). In term of the principles of operant conditioning, the observed increase in Behavior confirmed that positive attention was a Reinforcing Consequence as hypothesized.

O'Leary, Becker, Evans, and Saudargas (1969) extended the evaluation of Reinforcement in a study of **classroom token systems**. This study was designed to evaluate conditions when "...the teacher's use of praise and social censure is not effective" (p. 3). A second grade classroom of 21 students, in which 7 students were considered to be "disruptive", was selected for this investigation. This defined classroom conditions much more severe than those of the Masden et al. (1968) study, defined by 1 or 2 disruptive students in a given classroom. To establish a baseline of classroom behavior, the selected students were observed for 20 minutes a day. After a 20 second observation period, a 10 second period was used to record observed disruptive behaviors based on the following categories:

- Motor Behaviors: "Wandering around the room."

- Aggressive Behaviors: "Hitting, kicking, striking another child with an object."

- Disturbing Another's Property: "Grabbing another's book, tearing up another's paper."

- Disruptive Noise: "Clapping, stamping feet."

- Turning Around: "Turning to the person behind or looking to the rear of the room when the teacher was in front of the room."

- Verbalization: "Talking to others when not permitted by the teacher, blurting out answers, name calling."

- Inappropriate Tasks: "Doing one lesson (arithmetic) during the time specified for another (spelling)."

In addition to 3 conditions similar to those of the Masden et al. (1968) investigation (i.e., Classroom Rules, Educational Structure, Teacher Praise), a token program was established by O'Leary et al. (1969). Children in the class were told that they would receive points or ratings each afternoon, ranging from 1 to 10 and that "...the points would reflect the extent to which they followed the rules placed on the blackboard". The points were recorded on a small book at each child's desk, and the earned points were exchangeable for "...back-up reinforcers such as candy, pennants, dolls, comics, barrettes, and toy trucks" (p. 6). Initially, one of the researchers sat in the room and rated the children "...based on improvement in behavior". Points were awarded based on these ratings. The following guidelines were used:

- For marked improvement, the student received a rating between 8 and 10.

- If moderate improvement was shown, the child received a rating between 5 and 7 which would allow the student to earn at least a small prize by the end of the day.

- If the student was disruptive and did not evidence any improvement, a rating between 1 and 5 was given.

O'Leary et al. (1969) established this procedure as a compromise: "Although such a rating system involves much subjective judgement, it is relatively easy to implement, and a subsidiary aim of the study was to assess whether a token system could be implemented by one teacher in a class of average size" (p. 6). This procedure proved to be practical: after one week of training, the teacher was able to implement the token system without help from the investigators.

A high rate of disruptive student behavior was documented in the baseline condition: disruptive behavior occurred in 50% to 60% of the observation intervals. The conditions recommended by the Masden et al. (1968) study (Rules, Structure, Praising and Ignoring) were effective in 3 of the 7 disruptive students of this study. However, the initial effect in 2 of these very difficult students deteriorated rapidly and "...other children appeared to observe these boys being disruptive, with little or no adversive consequences, and soon became disruptive themselves. Several students were so disruptive that the academic pursuits of the class became impossible. The situation became intolerable and the Praise and Ignore Phase had to be discontinued" (p. 9). Apparently, the targeted children in this study were more difficult than those in the Masden et al. (1968) study, and the classroom behavior of 6 of the 7 disruptive students in this study did not change significantly when first 3 conditions were implemented.

When the Token system was initiated, the high rates of disruptive behavior dropped significantly (from over 50% to about 25%). When the Token system was withdrawn, the high rates of disruptive behavior returned, and when the Token system was reestablished the disruptive behavior again dropped significantly.

An A-B-C analysis of the O'Leary et al. (1969) study indicates that when Praise is not sufficient as a Reinforcing Consequence, a classroom tokens reinforcement program may offer an effective alternative. The change in Consequences (Tokens and Back-up Reinforcement) did result in an increase in the targeted Behavior (Appropriate or Nondisruptive Behavior in the classroom) in the specific Antecedent conditions (a classroom with 7 of 21 students having behavior problems).

This early study of behavior modification addressed 2 important issues (generalization and maintenance) which still represent major concerns about the use of token reinforcement programs in the classroom setting.

The issue of generalization was addressed because the Token Reinforcement Program was used by the teacher each afternoon but not each morning. This was dictated by the daily schedule, in which seatwork and reading groups were conducted in the morning. The teacher "...felt it would be disruptive to the rest of the class to interrupt reading groups to praise children who were doing independent work at theirs seats" (p. 13). When the Token system was introduced (in the afternoon), the disruptive behavior of children in the morning classroom showed an initial small decrease (from about 70% to about 50%), but this was not maintained. This was in stark contrast to the significant decrease in disruptive behavior of the same students with the same teacher in the afternoon, when the Token system was in effect. Based on these observations, O'Leary et al. (1969) offered the following comments:

> • The students "...presumably learned to discriminate that their appropriate behavior was reinforced only in the afternoon."
>
> • The differences in the children's behavior "...between the morning and the afternoon help to stress the point that 'generalization' is not magical process, but rather a behavioral change which must be engineered like any other change."
>
> • To accomplish generalization "...the teacher's response to disruptive behavior must remain constant throughout the day".

The issue of maintenance was addressed by establishing a Follow-up Condition, in which the initial Token system was replaced by a much simpler "systematic star system" (p. 7) which had the following characteristics:

> • Students received from 1 to 3 stars for good behavior twice during the morning and once during the afternoon.
>
> • Extra stars were awarded for good behavior when the class entered the room in the morning and afternoon and had restroom breaks.
>
> • A group contingency for boys and girls was used as a back-up reinforcer: if a child had 10 or more stars at the end of a day, a gold star was placed on a wall chart, and at the end of the week, each member of the group with the most gold stars received a piece of candy.
>
> • This use of stars, peer pressure, and a small amount of candy established a simple form of token reinforcement that could be implemented by any teacher.

The Follow-up token program was effective in maintaining decreased disruptive behavior, ranging "...from 8% to 39% lower during the Follow-up than during the Praise and Ignore phase of the study" (p. 10).

This classic study by O'Leary et al. (1969) demonstrated the use of practical, cost-effective behavior modification programs in the classroom based on simple token reinforcement programs. This basic approach provides the rationale for the important classroom component the UCI-CDC intervention methods described in Swanson (1988) and Swanson et al. (1990) and presented in Appendices C and D of this book.

The Masden et al. (1968) and O'Leary et al. (1969) studies represent the early work of a very influential group of investigators. A more recent example of their experimental work on Reinforcement is provided by Pfiffner, Rosen, and O'Leary (1985), who investigated the **efficacy of an all-positive approach to classroom management** in a special laboratory school (the Point of Woods Laboratory School) affiliated with the State University of New York (SUNY) at Stony Brook.

The Pfiffner et al. (1985) investigation followed the study by Rosen, O'Leary, Joyce, Conway, and Pfiffner (1984) on the importance of "prudent negative consequences" (which will be discussed in more detail in the next section on the operant conditioning principle of Punishment).

Rosen et al. (1984) contrasted "regular" positive consequences (e.g., verbal praise, bonus work, posting work) and negative consequences (e.g., verbal reprimands, time-out, withdrawal of privileges). When teachers stopped using negative feedback to students who had been functioning successfully with a combination of positive and negative consequences, the students' academic and social behavior deteriorated. This result questioned the effectiveness of an "all-positive" approach to classroom management.

Pfiffner et al. (1985) suggested that "...it seems unwarranted to conclude that a positively managed classroom is not possible unless the finding holds when a potentially more powerful incentive system is used" (p. 257).

The important addition to the Pfiffner et al. (1985) study was an "enhanced" set of positive consequences. This included an increased frequency of the "regular" positive (verbal praise, bonus work, posting work, etc.) plus additional positive such as "...songtime, special recess activities, posting work on a 'superstar' board, being allowed to read comic books, playing musical instruments, writing stories, and drawing" (p. 259). The "regular" positive condition was implemented in 2 ways: either alone or in combination with prudent negatives (verbal reprimands, time-out, removal of work, loss of recess time, etc.). The "enhanced" positive condition was not paired with the prudent negative condition.

The study was conducted on 8 students (5 second graders and 3 third graders) in the Point of Woods Laboratory School at SUNY Stony Brook. This laboratory setting allowed for the experimental manipulation of teacher behavior as an independent variable. In the "regular" positive condition, the number of positive teacher comments to the class was about 25 to 30 per hour. In the "enhanced" positive condition, the number of positive teacher comments to the class increased significantly and was maintained at about 60 per hour.

Observations of on-task behavior were taken, and several reversal of the 3 conditions (Regular Positive Alone, Regular Positive and Negatives, Enhanced Positive Alone) were implemented. The final condition revealed that on-task behavior improved from about 60% in the Regular Positive condition up to 86% in the Enhanced Positive condition and 93% in the Regular Positive and Negative condition. Pfiffner et al. (1985) concluded that enhanced positive alone "...are nearly as good" as the combination of regular positive and negative consequences, and that the limitation of an all-positive programs based on praise alone "...does not hold when a powerful and individualized incentive system is used" (p. 260).

8.4 Examples of Punishment

O'Leary, Kaufman, Kass, and Drabman (1970) investigated the effects of reprimands as **Punishment** for disruptive behavior in the classroom setting. This work was initiated to identify alternative for teachers to manage classroom behavior "...when praise and ignoring are not effective", and it focused on "... one alternative to ignoring disruptive behavior: reprimanding the child in a soft manner so that other children in the classroom could not hear the reprimand" (p. 146).

In an earlier study, Thomas, Becker, and Armstrong (1968) suggested that loud reprimands (e.g., yelling across the room to admonish a child for standing up and to give a command to sit down) are ineffective and may even be counterproductive in the long-term. With appropriate experimental control, O'Leary et al. (1970) observed and manipulated the percentage of loud and soft reprimands teachers directed towards disruptive students, and the results of the study led to the following conclusions:

> • When observed for baseline recording, "...almost all reprimands were found to be of a loud nature".
>
> • When teachers used "...soft reprimands, the frequency of disruptive behavior declined in most of the children".
>
> • When teachers used loud reprimands, "...a consequent increase in disruptive behavior was observed".

An A-B-C analysis of these results suggests that soft reprimands are Punishing Consequences (since the disruptive behavior they follow decreases over time), but that loud reprimands do not meet the technical definition of Punishment.

94

Van Houten et al. (1982) extended the work of O'Leary et al. (1970) on reprimands by evaluating the influence of **proximity of the teacher to the student**. Verbal reprimands were delivered from 1 meter away (soft, with physical contact) or from 7 meters away (hard, without physical contact). The results revealed that "...reprimands delivered from one meter away were considerably more effective than reprimands delivered from seven meters away" (p. 5).

Rosen, O'Leary, Joyce, Conway, and Pfiffner (1984) investigated the impact of **positive and negative consequences** on on-task behavior and academic behavior of hyperactive children in a classroom setting. A combination of both positive consequences (intended as Reinforcement) and negative consequences (intended as Punishment) was effective in maintaining on-task and productive performance. However, when the negative consequences were withdrawn, positive consequences alone were not sufficient to maintain appropriate behavior of these children in the classroom setting. An A-B-C analysis suggests that the negative consequences used in this study qualify as Punishment, but the mild ("regular") positive consequences did not qualify as Reinforcement.

Rosen et al. (1984) emphasized qualitative differences in punishment, by contrasting the effects of **prudent negative consequences** (reprimands delivered in a calm, concrete, and consistent fashion) with **imprudent negative consequences** (reprimands delivered in a loud, emotional, and inconsistent fashion). This was an important contrast, because the usual style of delivering negative consequences may be imprudent rather than prudent (O'Leary et al., 1970). The results of the Rosen et al. (1984) study indicated that "...when imprudent negatives were used, the classroom behavior deteriorated dramatically" (p. 601). Based on an A-B-C analysis, imprudent negative consequences do not qualify as Punishment.

In some behavioral classroom interventions, token reinforcement systems are used to provide Punishment by subtracting tokens for inappropriate behavior. This procedure is called **Response Cost**. Rapport, Murphy, and Bailey (1982) performed a study to contrast the effects of a simple response cost program to the effects of stimulant medication (Ritalin). A simple apparatus was developed, based on 2 wooden stands with 20 cards attached, numbered in descending order from 20 to 1. One wooden stand was kept on the teacher's desk, and the other was placed on the student's desk. During a period of seatwork (1 hour, divided into 3 20-minute intervals), the student was informed that up to 20 minutes of free time could be earned for working hard. The wooden stands were used to keep track of time-on-task. The student started with 20-minutes of free time, but lost 1-minute on each occasion when the teacher observed off-task behavior (i.e., not attending to the seatwork such as arithmetic problems). The teacher flipped a card on the wooden stand to keep track of off-task behavior, and the student was instructed to match the teacher's count on the wooden stand at the desk.

Before the Response Cost program was initiated, the students in this experiment were completing 60% or less of their assignments during the 1 hour seatwork period. When the Response Cost program produced a significant improvement in on-task behavior (up to 90%) and in completion of work (also up to 90%). A comparison of the Response Cost and Ritalin treatments demonstrated "...that both interventions produce positive changes in academic completion rates, with the response cost program resulting in higher and more stable responding" (p. 212).

In this study, the Punishment procedure (Response Cost) was very effective in raising levels of on-task behavior and in improving academic performance of ADD children.

96

The standard form of Punishment in most behavioral programs is **Time Out from Positive Reinforcement**. In a token reinforcement program, Time Out is based on removing (for a short period of time) the opportunity to earn points (reinforcement). Often Time Out is reserved for serious disruptive behavior which requires that the student be removed from the classroom and isolated in a Time Out room.

The use of Time Out is controversial (Gast and Nelson, 1977). This is a Punishment procedure that should work only when an effective positive reinforcement program is operating, so that removal of the opportunity to earn points is a meaningful negative consequence to the student. In some instances, the use of Time Out may act as a reinforcement rather than as a punishment. Time Out is often used because of its immediate effect of stopping ongoing behavior, but peer recognition or other source of Reinforcement may operate to produce a long-term effect of maintaining the behavior it is intended to prevent.

For these reason, the UCI CDC programs have not emphasized the use of Time Out. In fact, an administrative decision was made to severely limit (if not ban) the use of Time Out, in order to emphasize early intervention with other methods (Response Cost, Soft Reprimands, Ignoring, Increased Positive Reinforcement of Incompatible Behavior, etc.). Early recognition and intervention is effective in avoiding the escalation of behavior which would require Time Out if left unchecked.

Presentation of the detailed procedures for avoiding or limiting the use of Time Out in a school-based program is beyond the scope of this introductory manual. These details will be presented in an advanced manual which will be prepared in the future by other staff members of the UCI-CDC.

97

8.5 Examples of Extinction

Becker (1971) provided an example of extinction in the classroom setting. This example is somewhat controversial, since it is based on the premise that consequences intended to be negative (loud reprimands) may actually be Reinforcing Consequences rather than Punishing Consequences (Thomas et al., 1968). Becker (1971) provides an excellent example of the empirical process used to define Reinforcement and Punishment. The example is based on the hypothesis that, under the Antecedent conditions of certain classroom settings, the negative attention of loud reprimands can be Reinforcing. Based on this hypothesis, withholding reinforcement (Ignoring) should result in Extinction of the targeted Behavior.

Becker's (1971) example of Extinction, presented in his excellent book on behavior therapy, *Parents Are Teachers* (which has been used at the UCI-CDC for many years as the text for a parent education class on behavior modification), is based on a problem encountered in a large first grade class: a teacher was having problems with students *standing up* when they were required by classroom rules to remain seated. As a result, the teacher was frequently admonishing or reprimanding offending students to *sit down*. Loud reprimands would result in the offending student immediately sitting down, but over time many students continued to break the rules and to stand up frequently.

Becker (1971) described several investigations which were conducted to determine whether the Consequence for standing up (a loud reprimand from the teacher) technically should be classified as a Reinforcement or a Punishment.

98

In the context of the A-B-C framework, the *Antecedent* in this example was defined as **being in the large classroom.** The *Behavior* was specified as **standing up** when staying seated was required. The *Consequence* was defined as the teacher's command to **sit down.**

A baseline was taken to determine how often the students in the class were standing up (about 3 students every 10 seconds) and how often the teacher was saying sit down (about 21 times per hour). Then, the teacher was asked to increase the frequency of the Consequence (commanding students to *sit down*). Even though the short-term effect seemed favorable (students would immediately sit down), the long-term effects of these loud reprimands were unfavorable. Over several days this classroom manipulation (increasing the commands to sit down) resulted in students **standing up more often** (every 10 seconds, about 4.5 students got out of their seats). Based on the A-B-C framework, the loud reprimands technically were Reinforcing Consequences since the Behavior that they followed became more likely over time when the Antecedents were reestablished.

If the loud reprimands were reinforcing *standing up*, then withholding the Reinforcing Consequence should result in Extinction of the Behavior. To test this hypothesis, the teacher was instructed to stop using the loud reprimand (i.e., stop saying **sit down**) as a consequence of students standing up. The teacher was told to ignore the offending student and to notice students who were remaining seated instead. This classroom manipulation resulted in students standing up less often. Over time, after changing the Consequences in this way, on the average only 2 students every 10 seconds were *standing up.*

Technically, the A-B-C analysis of this experiment identified the teacher's command to sit down (the *Consequence*) as a **reinforcement** for standing up (the *Behavior*). Of course, this was not the teacher's intention, who meant this admonishment as a punishment to stop standing up behavior of the class. Becker (1971) called this the Criticism Trap. The teacher's commands to sit down (the Consequences) were having exactly the opposite long-term effect on *standing up* (the Behavior) than intended by the teacher or suggested by the immediate effect on the offending students. It is likely that peer recognition was operating to reinforce the "offending" student.

To avoid situations like the Criticism Trap, careful A-B-C analyses should be performed to document long-term effects of classroom manipulations (Consequences).

The example from Becker (1971) is offered as a teaching example for discussing the principles of behavior modification. **It is not intended as a recommendation for a specific school-based intervention for ADD students.** This example has been discussed in the literature (Masden et al., 1968; Van Houten et al., 1982; Pfiffner et al., 1985). The specific example of teacher attention having such a potent effect on students' classroom behavior is controversial.

Other techniques, such as **soft reprimands** (O'Leary et al., 1970), **prudent negatives** (Rosen et al., 1984), and **response costs** (Rapport et al., 1982) are essential for optimally effective interventions with ADD students. A more detailed discussion of these techniques is provided in articles describing the UCI-CDC school-based interventions (see Appendix C and Appendix D).

The Masden et al. (1968) study was used earlier as an example of for the principle of Reinforcement. This study also provides an example of use of the principle of Extinction in an attempt to reduce disruptive behavior in elementary school classrooms. As discussed earlier, Masden et al. (1968) contrasted two Consequences: Praising Appropriate Behaviors (to increase them by Reinforcement) and Ignoring Inappropriate Behaviors (to decrease them by Extinction). The rationale for Ignoring was based on the hypothesis that peers may reinforce students who are reprimanded (by giggling, noticing, laughing, etc.), and as a result the teacher's "...attention to Inappropriate Behavior may serve to strengthen the very behavior it is intended to diminish" (p. 144). Teachers were instructed to ignore violations of rules which interfered with teaching or learning (unless a child was being hurt by another). This attempt to use Extinction failed to decrease the target behavior of the study, which were motor activity (getting up, running, etc.), verbal noise (talking, laughing, etc.), and off-task behavior (not following instructions). The discussion of this failure was interesting. Apparently, Learning to Ignore Inappropriate Behavior was difficult for teachers, and as a result they were not able to implement the Extinction procedure on a consistent basis.

As noted earlier, for most students with diagnoses of ADD, selective approving and ignoring are not effective enough to deal with the ADD symptoms manifested in the classroom setting. More intensive behavior modifications are usually required to reduce disruptive behavior and elicit productive behaviors of ADD students in the classroom (Pelham, 1989). The UCI-CDC interventions (Swanson, 1988; Swanson et al, 1990) are based on the use of such token reinforcement program developed and refined by Pelham and his colleagues (Pelham, 1989).

8.6 Examples of Stimulus Control

The principle of **Stimulus Control** suggests one reason why generalization is so difficult to achieve in token reinforcement programs. When token reinforcers are used in the classroom setting, situational dependencies are likely to develop for the targeted Behavior. For example, in the earlier discussion of the O'Leary et al. (1969) study, a teacher established different contingencies in the morning and afternoon. The disruptive students in the study apparently learned to discriminate that their behavior was reinforced only in the afternoon and adjusted their behavior in the classroom accordingly. This is an example of the principle of Stimulus Control.

If a specific teacher is associated with the Antecedents and Consequences, then students are likely to learn that the A-B-C contingencies operate only when that individual is present. If this occurs, then the teacher has become a discriminative stimulus. The student's may learn to manifest a high rate of appropriate behavior when the teacher (the discriminative stimulus) is present, but when the teacher is not present a low rate of appropriate behavior may be manifested. This is another example of the principle of Stimulus Control.

Marholin and Steinman (1977) investigated Stimulus Control in the classroom. Students were observed and reinforced during a 30-minute period when seatwork (completing written math problems) was assigned. In one condition, **on-task behavior** was reinforced by a token (a mark on a data card) and a positive comments when the child was appropriately engaged in academic work. In another condition, **academic rate** (number of problems attempted) and **accuracy** (percentage of problems completed correctly) were reinforced by tokens. The tokens were exchanged for a free-time activity period following the seatwork period.

102

Marholin and Steinman (1977) hypothesized that the 2 different roles of the teacher in the 2 token programs would produce different effects when the teacher left the room. They hypothesized that the process of monitoring students for task orientation (on-task) and disruptive (off-task) behavior was an integral part of the teacher becoming a discriminative stimulus.

Monitoring on-task and off-task behaviors requires the teacher to be present to make the observations and to award the tokens as the behaviors occur. In contrast, monitoring academic rate and accuracy by inspection of permanent products does not require constant monitoring and does not require the teacher's constant presence to be implemented. Marholin and Steinman (1977) hypothesized that the process the teacher used to monitor progress could be separated from the direct Antecedents experienced by the student. An analysis of the A-B-C relationship suggested a way (i.e., changing the target Behavior from on-task/off-task behavior to academic rate and accuracy) to avoid situational dependency due to the Stimulus Control associated with the teacher becoming a discriminative stimulus.

The children investigated in this study in a class of 19 students (10 to 12 years of age) who "...were in a special classroom because of academic and behavioral problems experienced in their regular classrooms" (p. 467). The 8 most disruptive and least task-oriented students were selected as subjects. The classroom task selected for the study was taken from the mathematics textbook currently being used in the classroom. While working math problems, these students were observed for 5 minutes at multiple times across the day. Each 5 minute period was divided into 20 intervals, of which 20 seconds were for observation and 10 seconds were for recording behavior as neutral, disruptive, or on-task.

Three categories of disruptive behavior were used:

> • "Motor disruption, including touching, hitting, pinching, pulling others, and throwing objects".
>
> • "Verbal disruption, including talking aloud to self, talking to other children during individual work, yelling, signing, and interrupting."
>
> • "Noise, including nonword sounds, such as tapping, humming, dropping objects, slamming books, and whistling."

The following examples of on-task behavior were specified:

> • "Getting out appropriate materials."
>
> • "Looking at books or other material."
>
> • "Turning to appropriate page of assignment."
>
> • "Writing answers to questions or working problems."
>
> • "Following teacher's general instructions."
>
> • "Appropriate looking at person talking."
>
> • "Talking with teacher."
>
> • "Waiting with hand raised."
>
> • "Waiting in response to teacher's prompt."

Observations of on-task behavior in the classroom and measurements of academic productivity based on the permanent products of written work were taken in this study. Probe condition were utilized to document on-task behavior and academic productivity when the teacher was not in the room.

The probe conditions of the Marholin and Steinman (177) study revealed that "...the two contingency systems had a clearly differential effect on the children's academic rate. There were decreases of 54% and 79% in the teacher's absence when on-task behavior had been reinforced, compared to minimal decreases of 17% and 12% when accuracy and rate were reinforced" (p. 474).

This study demonstrates how the principle of Stimulus Control can be used to design a behavior modification program. The results indicate that "..by providing contingencies for the **products of the child's classroom activities** (i.e., academic achievement), rather than for some measure of the orientation or appropriate social behavior, the child will become more independent of the teacher's continual surveillance. Moreover, the child will come more under control of the academic materials themselves, rather than of the academic material and teacher presence" (p. 477).

The selection of target behaviors goes beyond the issue of stimulus control. When dealing with "normal" classes, O'Leary (1972) pointed out that it would be unreasonable to focus on "...disruptive behaviors, because by definition disruptive behaviors would mot exist or would exist at extremely low rates" (p. 507). However, when "problem" children, it is essential to focus on disruptiveness that impedes "...academic performance and/or the progress of other members of the class".

8.7 Examples with ADD Students

One of the first reports of a long-term behavior modification program specifically for ADD children was by O'Leary, Pelham, Rosenbaum, and Price (1976). Children (9 to 12 years of age) were selected on the basis of high scores (over 15) on the Conners Teacher rating scale. Two groups were established: a behavioral treatment group of 9 students and a control group of 8 students. None of these children were on stimulant medication while they were participating in this study. The behavioral treatment was a home-based reward program with 5 components:

- Specification of each child's daily goals

- Praising the child for efforts to achieve those goals

- End-of-day evaluation of the child's behavior relevant tot he specified goals

- Sending the parents a daily report card on the child's daily progress.

- Rewarding of the child by the parent for progress toward goals.

The behavior therapist met for 1 hour with the teacher to choose the behavioral goals of the program. O'Leary et al. (1976) described the result of teacher consultation in the following way: "Examples of goals chosen were: completing assigned math, helping neighbor with class project, not fighting, bringing in homework. We did not reinforce the children directly for sitting still, attending, or not fidgeting. Instead, academic and prosocial goals were given priority as most salient behaviors to be changed" (p. 512).

The behavior therapist met with each child's parents to explain the program and to select a suitable reward. O'Leary et al. (1976) gave the following examples of daily rewards for good report cards: "...30 minutes extra television, a special desert, spending time with either parent playing a game such as checkers, money to spend". Weekly rewards were also set, such as "... a fishing trip, dinner at a relative's house, a family meal at a fast food restaurant". A 10-week treatment program was used in this study. An individualized list of "problem behaviors" and the average item rating (from 0 to 3) on Conners Teacher Rating Scale were used to evaluate the treatment group and the control group before and after the behavior modification program was implemented. Across the 2 (pre/post) measurement times, the treatment group showed a large and statistically significant decrease in problems behaviors (from 5.5 to 3.0) and teacher ratings (from 2.0 to 1.2). The control group showed essentially no change.

These results led O'Leary et al. (1976) to conclude that "behavior therapy can be effective for hyperkinesia". They emphasized that behavior therapy could be an alternative to treatment with stimulant mediation, and commented that "...it is curious that, although drugs such as Ritalin are recommended 'as adjunctive therapy to other remedial measures' in the treatment of hyperkinesis, an all-too-common practice seems to be that of medicating these children to the exclusion of other remedial measures" (p. 513).

This book is not intended to contrast the effects of behavior modification and stimulant medication. Many studies have addressed this complicated issue, and a review of this literature is provided by Pelham (1989). However, 2 early investigations of this issue (Pelham, 1977; Loney et al., 1979) will be presented, because they provide excellent examples of effective behavioral programs for ADD children.

Pelham (1977) presented a case study which demonstrated the use of behavior therapy as an alternative to treatment with stimulant medication. This study extended the O'Leary et al. (1976) study by establishing a "...direct comparison of pharmacological and behavioral approaches in terms of their overall clinical effectiveness", and by extending the behavioral treatment so that it represented "...a relatively long-term intervention" (p. 474).

The subject for this study was 9 year old boy (J.T.) who had a diagnosis of hyperkinesis from a pediatric neurologist and had been on methylphenidate (Ritalin) for 3 years. The behavioral treatment started when the child was still being treated with medication. The behavioral intervention with the parents focused on "...two goals: (1) giving J.T. more attention for positive behaviors; and (2) first discriminating between mildly bothersome and significantly deviant behaviors, and ignoring the former and responding in a consist and mildly punitive fashion to the latter" (p. 475). The teacher "...was encouraged to give him attention when he engaged in appropriate behaviors and to ignore or consistently and mildly punish his disruptive behaviors. A home-based reward program was established (O'Leary, Rosenbaum, & Price (1976)" (p. 475). The goals of the behavioral program were selected by J.T.'s teacher and "...were (a) not disrupting the class, (b) not yelling at the teacher, and (c) completing his assigned tasks". For each positive report card, J.T. received a nickel.

The baseline (off medication) teacher rating (on a 0 to 3 scale) was 1.6 (2 SD above the mean). After 14 weeks of behavior therapy, during which medication was gradually withdrawn, the teacher rating decreased to .7 (only slightly above the mean). Pelham (1977) concluded that "...for this child, a stimulant drug could be withdrawn and effectively replaced with a behavioral program" (p. 74).

Loney, Weissenburger, Woolson, and Lichty (1979) used many of the behavior modification principles described in the prior sections. Children (between the ages of 6 and 12 years) referred to a psychiatry clinic were investigated in this study which compared the effects of behavioral intervention to the standard pharmacological intervention with stimulant medication. Diagnosis of the pre-DSM-III ADD equivalent ("hyperkinesis") was confirmed by extreme teacher and parent ratings (above 15 on the Conners 10-item Hyperkinesis Index), by interview about symptoms (overactivity, distractibility, impulsivity, and excitability), and by direct observation of off-task behavior in the classroom setting. Twelve "hyperkinetic" boys were selected, with 8 assigned to the behavior treatment and 4 to the medication treatment.

The behavioral treatment was based on "...consulting with the classroom teacher to (a) increase the ratio of approval to disapproval ("Catch the child being good"); decrease the intensity of those disapprovals that were delivered (O'Leary, Kaufman, Kass & Drabman, 1970); and (c) ignore off-task behavior when possible" (p. 137). The goal was to test a practical intervention with the following characteristics:

> • It relied "...on social reinforcers (approval and disapproval) rather than material ones (candy, prizes)".
>
> • It avoided "... techniques that required the teacher to read books or record behavior, that relied on electronic devices, or that removed the child from the average classroom or subjected him to peer pressure (group contingency techniques)".
>
> • It was "...inexpensive, simple, and built upon the use of positive reinforcement (praise)" (p. 138).

Pre and Post intervention observations of off-task and on-task behavior in the classroom were used to compare the effects of an 8 to 10 week behavioral intervention to standard pharmacological treatment. Before treatment, observations of % on-task behavior was similar for both groups (about 60%). Both treatments improved on-task behavior the same amount (to about 80%), which approximated the observations of on-task behavior in "average" students in each class (almost 90%). Loney et al. (1978) concluded "...statistically significant treatment effects were found for both drug-treated and behaviorally treated hyperkinetic boys; the size of these effects did not differ between the two types of treatment" (p. 133).

The practical nature of the behavioral intervention was emphasized by Loney et al. (1979). They offered these observations: "It appears as if consulting with the classroom teacher to deliver contingent social reinforcers to the hyperkinetic child during the ordinary school day can be feasible and effective, at least in the short run. The Masden approach to behavior modification is based on increasing the ratio of teacher approvals too disapprovals to 80%, and it is seen by most teachers as both humanistic (it 'accentuates the positive') and realistic (one is supposed to provide *some* disapprovals). Our experience is that teachers are responsive to this approach" (p. 141).

In addition to documenting the beneficial effects of behavioral intervention on the targeted students, Loney et al. (1979) observed 3 comparison children (an "overactive", "average", and "model" child) in each classroom. The behavioral treatment (but not the drug treatment) had a **spillover** effect on the other children who were not the direct targets of behavioral interventions in the classroom. These classmates showed increases in on-task behavior which may have been associated with treatment-induced changes in general teaching style.

9. UCI-CDC PROCEDURES

9.1 ABC's for ADD

The examples provided in Chapter 8 provide the basis of the behavior modification programs of the UCI-CDC school-based interventions. The examples selected certainly represent a selective rather than an exhaustive review. The detailed reviews of these classic studies were designed to present a historical perspective on the development of school-based interventions. Also, the detailed descriptions the selected investigations were designed to review the technical terms and jargon necessary to discuss the principles of operant conditioning and the techniques of behavior modification which have been applied in the UCI-CDC school-based settings.

There are several features of the techniques described in the prior Chapter which have been emphasized in the UCI-CDC programs, including the following:

> • At the UCI-CDC, a Reinforcement strategy was emphasized to foster appropriate behaviors (Masden et al., 1968; Loney et al., 1979; Pfiffner et al., 1985) rather than a Punishment strategy to eliminate inappropriate behaviors (Rosen et al., 1984; Rapport et al., 1984).
>
> • At the UCI-CDC, the use of material back-up reinforcers (O'Leary et al., 1969) has been minimized, and the use of preferred activities as back-up reinforcers (Becker, 1971; Loney et al., 1979; Pelham et al., 1980) has been maximized.

A common behavior modification strategy to change a problem behavior is to **define target behaviors which are incompatible with attention deficits in the classroom.** Instead of emphasizing Punishment (to decrease the problem behavior), Reinforcement should be emphasized (to increase an incompatible behavior).

In the UCI-CDC programs, the following 5 target behaviors (adapted from Pelham et al. (1980) are used to specify **the targets for intervention stated as appropriate activities for a typical class period:**

* **getting started** when instructed;

* **staying on task** for the entire period;

* **interacting** appropriately with peers and staff;

* **completing** the assigned work;

* **stopping and cleaning** up when class period ends.

Reinforcing Consequences are presented consistently whenever these target behaviors occur. According to the basic principles of operant conditioning, ADD symptoms (which are incompatible with these target behaviors) should decrease.

Different types of reinforcers are used in the UCI-CDC programs, including **social reinforcers** in the manner described in the earlier discussion of the Masden et al. (1968) and Pfiffner et al. (1985) studies, and **token reinforcers** in the manner described in the earlier discussion of the O'Leary et al. (1969), Rosen et al. (1984), Rapport et al (1982), and Marholin and Steinman (1977) investigations.

The UCI-CDC programs emphasize access to preferred activities to back-up reinforcers for tokens (Becker, 1971). This strategy is based on the Premack Principle which states that high frequency activities (play) can be used to reinforce low frequency activities (work). Becker (1971) has called this Grandma's Rule: first you work and then you play. At the UCI-CDC access to high frequency activities (e.g., computer games, arts and crafts, etc.) are used to increase the low frequency activities (e.g., attention in the classroom, completion of classwork, etc.) manifested by ADD students in the classroom setting.

At the UCI-CDC, techniques for awarding points to build up a total (reinforcement) and for subtracting points from an initial total (punishment) have been tried. Based on the literature (see Loney et al., 1979) and experience, a consensus has been reached that a ratio of 80% reinforcement to 20% punishment produces the best results with ADD students.

9.2 An Example Token System

As discussed in earlier sections, different types of events (Consequences) can be used to reinforce specific activities (Behaviors) in the classroom. In some instances, simple praise increases the behavior it follows, thus meeting the technical definition of Reinforcement (Masden, Becker, and Thomas, 1968; Pfiffner et al., 1985). Tokens increase the behavior they follow, so they too meet the definition of Reinforcement (O'Leary and Drabman, 1971). Soft reprimands (O'Leary et al., 1970) and prudent negative consequences (Rosen et al., 1984) meet the technical definition of Punishment, and these procedures are extremely efficient and effective when used in combination with positive consequences. Other procedures, such as Response Cost (Rapport et al., 1982) and Time Out (Barkley, 1990), meet the technical definition of Punishment, and these techniques may be necessary if the frequency and intensity of positive consequences or prudent negative consequences are not sufficient to produce appropriate behavior.

In the programs at the UCI-CDC, the number of tokens (points) delivered at the end of each class period is dependent upon the ADD student's behavior over that short period of time. From 0 to 4 points may be awarded, for each of the 5 behaviors (stated earlier). The number of points earned depends upon the degree to which the ADD student shows the target behaviors in the classroom. Perfect behavior earns 2 points for the first (*getting started*) and last behaviors (*stopping and transition*), which cover a brief part of the class period. For the target behaviors which must be continued for the entire class period (*staying on task, interacting with peers, completing work*), 4 points are awarded for perfect behavior. Based on this, up to 16 points (2+4+4+4+2) can be earned during each class period.

A simple bookkeeping method is used. At the end of each class period, points earned are recorded on a point sheet. An example point sheet, which has sections for rating of each target behavior for each period of the day, is shown below:

	Class Period								
Target Behavior	1	2	3	4	5	6	7	8	AVG
got started	__	__	__	__	__	__	__	__	___
stayed on task	__	__	__	__	__	__	__	__	___
interacted well	__	__	__	__	__	__	__	__	___
completed work	__	__	__	__	__	__	__	__	___
ready to change	__	__	__	__	__	__	__	__	___
Period AVG	__	__	__	__	__	__	__	__	___

This type of point sheet provides valuable information for the ADD student and the teacher. Difference in behavior in different class periods are reflected in the column totals, and differences in specific target behaviors (averaged across class periods) are reflected in the row totals.

This established token system is described in published articles (Swanson, 1988; Swanson et al., 1990) and in Appendices C and D. This token system was developed for the model school setting at UCI-CDC. In the next section, a modification of this approach is presented which is designed for general use in regular classroom settings in the public schools.

115

9.3 Links to the SKAMP

The purpose of the SKAMP was to define the presence of ADD symptoms manifested in the classroom. For that reason, the items of the SKAMP were written to specify Inappropriate Behavior. The UCI-CDC token reinforcement system reverses this emphasis: the target behaviors are defined as Appropriate Behavior (attention and deportment) in the classroom. In addition to the 5 target behaviors (getting started, staying on task, interaction with peers, and stopping), 5 related target behaviors were developed to better specify appropriate attention and deportment in the classroom: **remaining quiet** when required by class rules; **remaining seated** when required by class rules; **interacting appropriately** with teacher or aide; **performing written work** accurately and neatly; **directing effort** to class activities for entire period.

The 10 SKAMP items and the 10 target behaviors of the token system represent **opposite** Behaviors in an A-B-C analysis of classroom activities. In one case (the SKAMP items), Behavior is defined by presence of ADD symptoms in the classroom; in the other case (the target behaviors), Behavior is defined by the absence of ADD symptoms in the classroom. The goal of intervention is to create Antecedents and Consequences to increase the frequency of Behavior defined by the opposite of ADD symptoms as they are manifested in the classroom.

As the literature shows (e.g., O'Leary and Drabman, 1971; Pelham, 1989; Kazdin, 1989) token reinforcement programs provide a simple but powerful way to control classroom behavior of ADD children. As discussed in an earlier section, the basic techniques of behavior modification involve arranging the environment (the "A" and the "C" components of this simple A-B-C relationship) to change behavior.

116

By making *Reinforcement* (points earned) contingent upon specific behaviors, the frequency of those particular "B's" can be increased. By making *Punishment* (points lost) contingent upon specific behaviors, the frequency of those particular "Bs" can be decreased. The following list of Behaviors is recommended to specify the targets behaviors for a classroom behavior modification program for ADD students:

	No	Improved	Yes
• got started with the class	___	___ ___	___
• stayed on task	___	___ ___	___
• interacted well with peers	___	___ ___	___
• interacted well with staff	___	___ ___	___
• remained quiet when required	___	___ ___	___
• remained seated when required	___	___ ___	___
• completed work	___	___ ___	___
• attended to class activities	___	___ ___	___
• ready for transition	___	___ ___	___

As discussed earlier, these 10 target behaviors were written to represent the opposite (or incompatible) behaviors compared to the SKAMP items which specify the classroom manifestation of ADD symptoms. Based on the observation categories listed above, from 0 (for No) to 3 (for Yes) points can be awarded for Appropriate Behavior during a classroom period. This scoring procedure matches that of the SKAMP.

This 10-item list of target behaviors can be used to keep track of the points earned across the day. An example is shown below:

Target Behavior	Class Period								AVG
	1	2	3	4	5	6	7	8	
got started	__	__	__	__	__	__	__	__	__
stayed on task	__	__	__	__	__	__	__	__	__
peer interaction	__	__	__	__	__	__	__	__	__
staff interaction	__	__	__	__	__	__	__	__	__
remained quiet	__	__	__	__	__	__	__	__	__
remained seated	__	__	__	__	__	__	__	__	__
completed work	__	__	__	__	__	__	__	__	__
maintained effort	__	__	__	__	__	__	__	__	__
ready for change	__	__	__	__	__	__	__	__	__
Period AVG	__	__	__	__	__	__	__	__	__

The entry in each blank on this form would represent the number of points earned (from 0 to 3) for a class period. Thus, up to 30 points per class period could be earned if perfect behavior were manifested. On this form, row totals represent the average behavior across periods, and column totals represent the behavior for each period averaged across the 10 target behaviors.

9.4 Back-up Reinforcers

The points of the UCI token system do not automatically operate as reinforcers to increase the five target behaviors. They gain this power from the ability to be exchanged for preferred activities either at home or at school. When the points are exchanged at home, the token system is called a **home based reinforcement** program. When the points are exchanged at school, the token system is called a **school based reinforcement program**. Of course, arrangements can be made to allow exchanges can take place in both settings.

In the UCI program, back-up reinforcers are provided during a 15 to 30 minute period at the end of each day at school. Access to back-up reinforcer is based on the percentage of points:

•   Children who earn below 80% select from low priority activities (e.g., reading a book, sitting quietly, drawing with a ruler);

•   Children who earn at least 80% but less than 90% select from low or middle priority activities (e.g., playing with clay, watching other children play computer games, drawing with crayons or felt pens).

•   Children who earn 90% or more select from low, middle or high priority activities (e.g., playing computer games, using board games, working on special art projects).

9.5 Shaping and Prompting

In classroom behavioral programs, the behavior of the teacher is extremely important (Thomas et al. (1968; Pfiffner and Barkley, 1990). **The goal of the teacher should be to set the stage for the ADD student to earn at least 80% of the possible points.** There are several ways to reach this goal which involves changing the "A's" in the A-B-C relationship.

Consider an example for a child who has difficulty averting attention at the beginning (getting started) and end (stopping and shifting activities) of class periods. This should be reflected in the column totals at the end of the school day. The next day, the teacher should approach the ADD child before the period starts and give a reminder as an Antecedent for *getting started*:

> When you hear the instructions, get started right away and you will earn all of your points.

Just before the period ends, the teacher should instruct the ADD student to set the Antecedent for *stopping, cleaning up, and shifting activities:*

> When you hear my directions to the class, be sure to stop what you are doing right away, clean up and get ready for what we will do next period. Then you will earn all of your points.

Effective interventions with ADD students may require extra classroom staff (i.e., a classroom aide) to allow for an increase the frequency and intensity in the delivery of positive and negative consequences in the regular classroom. At UCI-CDC, shaping and prompting are essential procedures for implementing a classroom behavior modification program.

9.6 The Levels System

Progress in the UCI-CDC treatment program is associated with movement through 3 levels of treatment:

> • Level I intervention is based on continuous monitoring of and direct feedback to children using social reinforcers and tokens. An intensity sufficient to have an acute effect on the behavior is maintained (typically for two to three weeks) until success is achieved (defined as earning 90% of possible tokens).
>
> • Level II intervention is based on self-monitoring and self-evaluation (the *match game*). This is used to withdraw the continuous monitoring and is intended to foster generalization. The length of time to meet the criteria for matching has been variable, requiring from 4 to 10 weeks.
>
> • Level III intervention is based on responsibility/ privilege contingencies (which reflect the uncertainties of natural consequences in the real world environment) instead of the standard token system.

At the UCI-CDC, a levels system is used. The articles by Swanson (1988) and Swanson et al. (1990) provide a more detailed description of the coordination of clinical and educational interventions designed to move ADD children through a *levels system*. In Appendix C, this process is described, which starts with constant monitoring (Level 1), graduates to self-monitoring and self-evaluation (Level 2), and has as its long-term goal withdrawal of the token system and replacement with a responsibility privilege system (Level 3).

9.7 Emphasis on Reinforcement

It is clear that all-positive programs are effective but difficult to implement (Pfiffner et al., 1985). In the context of primarily positive consequences (i.e., 80% positive reinforcement), the use of negative consequences (i.e., 20% punishment) is very efficient, effective, and well accepted by teachers in the regular classoom (Loney et al. (1978).

The way the negative consequences are delivered is extremely important (Rosen et al., 1984; Van Houten et al., 1982; Rapport et al., 1982). The specific and important details about the use of negative consequences, such as soft reprimands and response cost, have been described in the previous section. The advice of O'Leary et al. (1970) provides an ideal guide: We "...do not recommend soft reprimands as an alternative to praise. An ideal combination would probably be frequent praise, some soft reprimands, and very occasional loud reprimands" (p. 155).

The use of intensive school-based behavior modification programs is not new. In fact, the UCI-CDC program is much like the school-based token programs O'Leary et al. (1969) and Walker and Buckley (1972) developed and used over 20 years ago. These classroom interventions have large effects. For example, Walker and Buckley (1972) selected problem students with low percentages of appropriate behavior in the classroom setting (under 45% by direct observation). The school-based token system increased this to the normal range of appropriate behavior (90%). At the UCI-CDC, similar large effects of classroom token systems have been consistently achieved over the past 7 years.

This has been accomplished with many changes in teaching and clinical staff, but with a consistent direction based on the principles and techniques of behavior modification which have been discussed in the previous sections of this book. The experience and the literature described in this book provide strong support for a dramatic and large effect of school-based behavior therapy delivered in classroom settings.

It is important to note that the impressive gains associated with token reinforcement systems have been manifested only in the short-term. Evidence for long-term gains is limited (Walker and Buckley, 1972; O'Leary and Schneider, 1977), but the principle of operant conditioning do suggest specific strategies to enhance generalization and maintenance (e.g., see Marholin and Steinman, 1977; Turkewitz, O'Leary, and Ironsmith, 1975; Swanson et al., 1990).

The UCI-CDC program was based on the hypothesis that careful design and long-term treatment is necessary to produce long-term effects of behavior modification. The initial programs (see Appendices C and D) were based on a full year of intensive intervention, including the generalization training based on self-monitoring and self-evaluation, followed by adaptation of behavioral programs for transition to the next placement.

Based on the new guidelines from the US Department of Education, the application of behavior modification programs for ADD students in the public school setting may increase. If the educational manifestation of ADD is viewed as a chronic problem, then long-term interventions should be developed. The school setting offers an ideal opportunity to provide the type of intervention, based on the principles of operant conditioning, to achieve long-term benefits.

10. Programs at UCI-CDC

10.1 Three Model Programs

The UCI-CDC staff have applied the general principles and techniques of behavior modification to formulate the 3 model programs for school-based interventions. These school-based multimodality treatment programs were designed to match the needs of the 3 groups of ADD students described in the PGARD response to the Notice of Inquiry:

> • the **parallel teaching** model, developed by Linda Pfiffner, alters the regular classroom to fit the needs of ADD children in PGARD Group I (with mild impairments).
>
> • the **paraprofessional** model, developed by Ronald Kotkin, Ph.D., provides additional resources in the regular classroom to meet the needs of ADD children in PGARD Group II (with moderate impairments).
>
> • the **multicomponent treatment model**, developed by Swanson et al. (1990), provides clinical and educational interventions in combination to meet the needs of ADD children in PGARD Group III (with severe impairments).

All 3 models are based on the assumptions that the attention and motivational problems of ADD students are manifested continuously throughout the day and require interventions which are applied throughout the day while the ADD child is in the school setting.

10.2 The Parallel Teaching Model

Pfiffner (1992) led the development of a program at UCI-CDC to train teachers to use frequent and brief specialized interventions blended with their regular teaching styles. Teachers are trained to do two things in parallel:

> • to conduct academic instruction (i.e., to carry out a lesson plan).
>
> • to scan the room and to provide redirection and reinforcement to the ADD student in a large class of non-ADD students.

The goal of parallel teaching is to increase frequency of teacher: child interaction by systematic applications of basic behavioral techniques: positive reinforcement (i.e., the *catch 'em being good* technique of Masden et al., 1968) to encourage attentive on-task behavior, and prudent negatives (i.e., the *catch 'em before getting bad* technique of Rosen et al., 1984) to avoid escalation of disruptive behaviors.

Training and practice is required to make these simple but powerful techniques become **second nature** to the teacher. Positive consequences (teacher attention, privileges, access to preferred activities, etc.) must be used to shape and maintain attentive behavior and completion of academic work, and **prudent negative consequences** must be timed and delivered early in the typical behavioral sequences which usually escalate and later require more severe negative consequences (e.g., time out). Detailed descriptions of the techniques for this approach are described in Pfiffner and Barkley (1990).

10.3 The Paraprofessional Model

In collaboration with the Irvine Unified School District (IUSD), the UCI-CDC staff developed this model program for moderately impaired ADD students who could be well-served by providing supplementary services delivered in the regular classroom. Kotkin et al. (1992) developed a program to train teachers' aides (paraprofessionals) and regular classroom teachers to use specific techniques which are effective with ADD students. The paraprofessional model is based on 3 methods of intervention:

• a classroom performance component, in which the paraprofessional works as a teacher's aide to facilitate the use of the parallel teaching model and to help implement a token economy with **frequent and consistent token reinforcers** (points) and potent activity reinforcers which are necessary for educationally impaired ADD students.

• a skills remediation component, conducted in small groups in which the paraprofessional uses **coaching** and continuous reinforcement to shape new social skills and language in the ADD child to facilitate classroom behavior modification.

• a daily report card component, which over a 12 week period replaces the intensive **point system** and allows the presence of the paraprofessional to be reduced and eventually faded out.

A more detailed description of the methods for this type of school-based intervention is provided in Appendix D.

10.4 The Multicomponent Model

In some ADD students, severe educational impairment exists. Usually, in these extreme cases students have an "ADD-Plus" condition (Shaywitz and Shaywitz, 1988; Swanson, 1988) defined by a coexisting specific learning disability (SLD) or serious emotional disturbance (SED). Often, these ADD students are referred at a time of crisis and placement in a self-contained classroom may be required (at least for a limited period of time).

The UCI-CDC staff (Swanson et al., 1990) developed an intensive multicomponent program which has 4 components:

> • intensive (6 hours per day) behavioral intervention conducted by a teacher and a behavioral specialist in a classroom of 12 to 15 ADD students;
>
> • daily skill training groups conducted by mixed clinical and educational staff (one counselor and the teacher or the aide);
>
> • careful double-blind assessments of pharmacological intervention which evaluates effects on learning as well as behavior;
>
> • parent involvement in group and individual meetings to extend the behavior modification program to the home setting.

This model represents an intensive combination of clinical and educational interventions for students with extreme ADD. A detailed description of it is provided in Appendix C.

10.5 Resources Required

Based on the paraprofessional model programs (Kotkin et al, 1992) developed by the UCI-CDC staff for the Irvine Unified School District (IUSD), an estimate was made of the resources necessary to implement ADD interventions on a school-wide basis.

The PGARD prevalence figures suggest that for a school with 600 students, about 10 to 12 of the students will have ADD with moderate impairment (those in PGARD Group II with moderate impairment who need the "second level" of school-based intervention based on the Paraprofessional Model).

In addition, a school-wide assessment should identify another 12 to 15 ADD students with mild or no impairment (those in PGARD Group I who need the "first level" of school-based intervention based on the Parallel Teaching Model) and 5 or 6 ADD students with severe impairment (those in PGARD Group III who need the "third level" of school-based intervention based on the Multicomponent Model).

To provide the paraprofessional intervention for 10 to 12 ADD students, it has been estimated that two half-time behavioral specialists (highly trained classroom aides) would be required. Twice a week, these moderately impaired ADD students, in groups of four, attend a 30 to 45 minute skill training group in which continuous reinforcement is used to shape new social and cognitive skills which ADD children often lack. Over a 6 to 12 week period, these groups are used to cover a curriculum designed to develop and practice specific skills (e.g., cooperation, communication, participation, validation, assertion without aggression, etc.) and rules (raising hand to talk, staying seated, following directions to a "T", etc.).

The paraprofessional who conducts the skill training group also returns to the classroom with the ADD students to serve as a classroom aide. Initially, the extra classroom aide time may amount to 15 hours per week (3 hours per day for 5 days per week) for each classroom containing one of more of the ADD students who are concurrently in the twice-a-week skill training group.

Group skill training <u>alone</u> does not have a significant impact of the academic performance or behavior of ADD children in the regular classroom (see Appendix D). Classroom effects are dependent upon the paraprofessional acting as a classroom aide to provide "reinforced practice" in the regular classroom. This seems to be essential to achieve generalization of targeted behavior of ADD students. Based on experience in the IUSD, the assignment of an extra aide to work with the targeted ADD student (as well as other students in the classroom) is a very cost-efficient way of delivering effective educational intervention for ADD students who require extra help in the school setting.

10.6 Emphasis on Behavior Therapy

This book emphasizes intervention based on the principles and techniques of behavior modification. My academic background did not prepare me to be an advocate of behavior therapy, but over the last 15 years I have become a staunch advocate anyway. In this section, I will provide some explanation of why I have made such a strong commitment to this approach.

My early work with ADD children focused on laboratory evaluation of the effects of stimulant medication on ADD children. With Marcel Kinsbourne, M.D., a brilliant pediatric neurologist, I published several technical papers on the specific effects of stimulants such as methylphenidate (Ritalin) on the learning of ADD children. Over a five year period at the Hospital for Sick Children in Toronto, we refined a medication assessment protocol based on double-blind assessments and cognitive laboratory tests (Swanson and Kinsbourne, 1978; Swanson, 1989; Kinsbourne, 1989).

In 1978, I was introduced to behavior therapy at the American Psychological Association which met in Toronto. K. Daniel O'Leary delivered the Presidential address to the Clinical Division, Section III. His talk, "Pills or Skills for Hyperactive Children", challenged my views that stimulant medication offered a long-term solution for treatment of ADD.   I met several times with Dan O'Leary's colleagues, Sue O'Leary and Bill Pelham, and these two individuals convinced me that behavior therapy along with stimulant medication would be essential for effective treatment of ADD children. Over the next two years, they were my mentors. They taught me the rudimentary techniques of behavior modification while I was at the Hospital for Sick Children.

In 1980, I move to the University of California, Irvine. In collaboration with Jeff Levine, a child psychiatrist who directed the child Inpatient Unit at the UCI Medical Medical Center, I started an intensive treatment program for severely affected ADD children, most of whom had comorbid disorders such as depression, anxiety, and conduct disorder. To help us implement a behavioral approach, we obtained the help of Bill Pelham and his student, Mary Bender, as consultants to train the staff of the Child Psychiatry Inpatient Unit. Chris Fiore, a student from California State University at Fullerton, emerged as the primary staff member who was committed to the behavioral apporach for the treatment of ADD children. We also hired Mary Bender to provide the expertise required to operate an intensive behavioral program for very disruptive ADD children.

A successful program was established and operated, but over a period of a year we realized the obvious: the hospital setting was not entirely appropriate for most of the ADD children we were treating, and generalization of behavioral programs to the natural environment after treatment was a significant problem. It was clear that a school setting would provide the best setting for intensive behavioral intervention, since ADD children (like most 5 to 12 year old children) spend so much of their time (about 6 hours per day) in that setting.

To create a school-based behavioral intervention, we adopted a day treatment approach patterned after Bill Pelham's Summer Treatment Program at Florida State. Chris Fiore and Joanne Wilson, a teacher who had been trained by Bill Pelham, assumed the major responsibility for the first ADD Summer Treatment Programs at UCI.

In 1985, after several successful Summer Programs, UCI provided adequate space in a 5,000 square foot building on the UCI campus to establish a year round school-based treatment program for ADD children. This became the UCI Child Development Center (CDC). To get the school started, I collaborated with a school psychologist, Steve Simpson, who became the major architect for the educational component of the UCI multimodality treatment program. Later, several psychologists (who had focused interests in ADD and expertise and training in behavior modification) were recruited to join the UCI-CDC staff, including Linda Pfiffner (who trained at Stony Brook with Sue O'Leary), Ron Kotkin (who trained as an educator and a psychologist at the University of Sourthern California and who was Steve Simpson's colleague in program at Chapman College), Tim and Sharon Wigal (who trained with Abe Amsel at tthe University of Texas at Austin), and Keith McBurnett (who trained with Ben Lahey at the University of Georgia). The medical input for this program came from Marc Lerner, a pediatrician who trained with Mel Levine, and Dennis Cantwell, a child psychiatrist from UCLA.

In the late 1980's, I met with the person most responsible for the theoretical basis for operant conditioning, B.F. (Fred) Skinner, to obtain his opinion about the applications of behavior modification in educational settings. This interaction led to revisions of the UCI-CDC program, based on some of the theoretical concepts expressed in Walden II (1948), and a better appreciation of the brillant theory of selection by consequences (Skinner, 1987) which I consider to be an intellectual accomplishment similar to Darwin's theory of natural selection. These meetings led to segments for a Television course on Introductory Psychology, which included an interview with Dr. Skinner about operant conditioning and which used the UCI-CDC program as an example of a clinical application of the principles of operant conditioning.

In the evaluations of ADD children at the UCI-CDC, parents and teachers often indicate that "behavior modification has been tried and does not work". Usually, a rigorously review of the way behavioral techniques have been applied reveal why prior interventions have not been successful.

In the area of school intervention which is emphasized in this book, the literature (Witt, 1986) indicates that in some cases, behavior modification programs are effective but are not applied due to teacher resistance. Witt (1986) identified several reasons for teacher resistance including excessive requirements of time and resources, incompatible theoretical orientation of the teacher, intrusiveness of the behavior modification program. In our experience, the most serious impediment to the use of behavior modification in the classroom is the lack of resources available to teachers to help add a special program for a few ADD students to existing classroom activities which are appropriate for the majority of the students. At UCI-CDC, we have developed the paraprofessional model to add the required resources when necessary (i.e., a part-time classroom aide trained in the techniques of behavior modification) to implement a standard behavior modification program for ADD students in the classroom setting.

Teachers willing to try simple classroom token reinforcement programs can be successful **if the classroom resources match the special needs of the ADD student.** Based on experience over many years, we expected that in about half of all ADD cases referred tot he UCI-CDC, the severity of educational impairment due to ADD symptoms will be too great to be altered significantly by the regular classroom teacher alone. To establish an effective behavior modification program for an ADD student with moderate to severe impairment, more frequent reinforcement is required to get things started than can be reasonably expected from a classroom teacher alone.

REFERENCES

Atkins, M, Pelham, WE, Licht, MH (1985). A comparison of objective classroom measures and teacher ratings of attention deficit disorder. J Abnor Child Psychol, 13, 155-167.

Atkins, M, Pelham, WE, Licht, MH (1988). The development and validation of objective classroom measures for conduct and attention deficit disorders. Advances in Behavioral Assessment of Children and Families, 4, 3-31.

Atkins, M, Pelham, WE, Licht, MH (1989). The differential validity of teacher ratings of attention/overactivity and aggression. J Abnor Child Psychol, 17, 423-435.

Atkins, M, Pelham, WE (1991). School-based assessment of attention deficit-hyperactivity disorder. J Learn Dis, 24, 197-204.

Barkley, RA (1977). A review of stimulant drug research with hyperactive children. J Child Psychol Psychiat, 18, 137-165.

Barkley, RA (1990). Attention-deficit Hyperactivity Disorder: A handbook for diagnosis and treatment. New York: Guilford Press.

Barkley, RA, Copeland, AP, & Sivage, C (1980). A self-control classroom for hyperactive children. J Autism Dev Disord, 10(1), 75-88.

Barkley, R, and Cunningham, C (1978). Do stimulant drugs improve the academic performance of hyperkinetic children? Clin. Pediat., 17, 85-92.

Becker, WC (1971). Parents are teachers: A child management program, Champaign, IL: Research Press.

Bellamy, GT (1987). Education for the Handicapped Law Report, 211:242. CCR Publishing Co: Axelandria, Virginia.

Bellamy, GT (1989). Education for the Handicapped Law Report, 213:194. CCR Publishing Co: Axelandria, Virginia.

Carlson, CL(1986). Attention deficit disorder without hyperactivity: a review of preliminary evidence. In BB Lahey & AE Kazdin (Eds), Adv Clin Child Psychol, 9, 153-175.

Carlson, CL, & Lahey, BB (1988). Behavior classroom interventions with children exhibiting conduct disorders or attention deficit disorders with hyperactivity. In JC Witt, SM Elliot, & FM Gresham (Eds.), The Handbook of Behavior Therapy in Education, (pp. 653-677). New York:Plenum Press.

Conners, CK (1969). A teacher rating scale for use in drug studies with children. Amer J Psychiat, 126, 884-888.

Council for Exceptional Children (1992). Children With ADD: A Shared Responsibility. Reston, VA.

Davila, RR, Williams, ML, & MacDonald, JT (1991). Clarification of policy to address the needs of children with Attention Deficity Hyperactivity Disorders within general and/or special education. (Memorandum from the US Department of Education: Office of Special Education and Rehabilitative Services).

Dent, H (1992). Presentation:CHADD Meeting, Chicago.

DSM-III (1980). American Psychiatric Association, Washington DC.

DSM-III-R (1987). American Psychiatric Association, Washington DC.

DSM-IV Options Book: Work In Progress (1991). American Psychiatric Association, Washington DC.

Forness, SR, Cantwell, DP, Swanson, JM, Hanna, GL, & Youpa, D (1991). Differential effects of stimulant medication on reading performance of boys with hyperactivity with and without Conduct Disorder. J Learn Disabil, 24, 304-310.

Fowler, M (1992). Educators Manual. CHADD: Fairfax

Gast, DL & Nelson, CM (1977). J Spec Educ, 11, 457-465.

Gordon, M (1983). The Gordon Diagnostic System. Boulder, CO: Clinical Diagnostic Systems.

Greenberg, LM (1991). TOVA Interpretation Manual. Minneaplois, MN: Author.

Hinshaw, SP (1987). On the distinction between attentional deficits/hyperactivity and conduct problems/aggression in childhood psychopathology. Psychol Bull, 101, 443-463.

Kavale, K (1982). The efficacy of stimulant drug treatment for hyperactivity: a meta analysis. J Learn Dis, 15, 280-289.

Kazdin, AE (1989). Behavior Modification in Applied Settings, Fourth Edition. Pacific Grove, CA: Brooks/Cole.

Kazdin, AE (1989). Developmental psychopathology: Current research, issues, and directions. Amer Psychol, 44, 180-187.

Kotkin, R (1992). Appendix to Multimodality Treatment Grant. Child Devlopment Center, UCI, Irvine, CA.

Lahey, BB, Hynd, GW, Carlson, CL, & Nieves, N (1987). Attention deficit disorder with and without hyperactivity: comparison of behavioral characteristics of clinic referred children. J. Am Acad Child Psychiat, 26, 718-723.

Lambert, NM, Sandoval, J, & Sassone, D (1978). Prevalence of hyperactivity in elementary school children as a function of social system definers. Amer J Orthopsychiatr, 48, 446-463.

Loney, J, & Milich, R (1982). Hyperactivity, inattention, and aggression in clinical practice. In M Wolraich & D Routh (Eds.), Advan Dev Behav Pediat (Vol. 3, pp. 113-147). Greenwich, CT: JAI Press.

Loney, J, Weissenburger, FE, Woolson, RF, & Lichty, EC (1979). Comparing psychological and pharmacological treatment for hyperkinetic boys and their classmates. J Abnor Child Psychol, 7, 133-143.

McBurnett, RK, Lahey, BB, & Swanson, JM (1991). Ritalin treatment in Attention Deficit Disorder without Hyperactivity. In L.L.Greenhill & B.B. Osman (Eds.), Ritalin: Theory and Patient Management. (257-263). New York: Liebert.

Masden, CH, Becker, WC, & Thomas, DR (1968). Rules, praise, and ignoring: elements of classroom control. J Applied Behav Anal, 1, 139-150.

Marholin, D & Steinman, WM (1977). Stimulus control in the classroom as a function of the behavior reinforced. J Applied Behav Anal, 10, 465-478.

O'Leary, KD (1972). Behavior modification in the classroom: a rejoinder to Winett and Winkler. J Applied Behav Anal, 5, 505-511.

O'Leary, KD (1980). Pills or skills for hyperactive children. J Applied Behav Anal, 13, 191-204.

O'Leary, KD, Becker, WC, Evans, MB, & Saudargas, RA (1969). A token reinforcement program in a public school: a replication and analysis. J Applied Behav Anal, 2, 3-13.

O'Leary, KD & Drabman, R (1971). Token reinforcement programs in the classroom: a review. Psychol Bull, 75, 379-398.

O'Leary, KD, Kaufman, KF, Kass, RE, & Drabman, RS (1970). The effects of soft and loud reprimands on the behavior of disruptive students. Excep Child, 37, 145-155.

O'Leary, KD & O'Leary, SG (1977). Classroom management: The successful use of behavior modification (2nd ed.). New York: Permagon Press.

O'Leary, KD, Pelham, WE, Rosenbaum, A, & Price, GH (1976). Behavioral treatment of hyperkinetic children. Clin Pediatrics, 15, 510-514.

O'Leary, SG, Schneider, MR (1977). Special class placement for conduct problem children. Exceptional Children, 24-30.

Ottenbacher, KJ & Cooper, MM (1983). Drug treatment of hyperactivity in children. Dev Med and Child Neurol, 25, 358-366.

Pelham, WE (1977). Withdrawal of a stimulant drug and concurrent behavioral intervention in the treatment of a hyperactive child. Behav Ther, 2, 473-479.

Pelham, WE (1989). Behavior therapy, behavioral assessment and psychostimulant medication in the treatment of attention deficit disorders: An interactive approach. In L Bloomingdale and JM Swanson (Eds.), Attention Deficit Disorder IV. New York: Pergamon Press.

Pelham, WE, Evans, SW, Gnagy, EM, & Greenslade, KE (1992). School Psychol Rev, 21, 285-299.

Pelham, WE, Milich, R, Murphy, D, & Murphy, HA (1989). Normative data on the IOWA-Conners teacher rating scale. J Clin Psychol, 18, 259-262.

Pelham, WE, Gnagy, EM, Greenslade, KE, & Milich, R (1992). Teacher ratings of DSM-III-R symptoms for the disruptive behavior disorders. J Am Acad Child Adolesc Psychiat, 31(2), 210-218.

Pelham, WE, Schnedler, RW, Bologna, N & Contreras, A (1980). Behavioral and stimulant treatment of hyperactive children: A therapy study with methylphenidate probes in a within-subject design. J Applied Behav Anal, 13, 221-236.

Pfiffner, LJ (1992). Appendix to Multimodality Treatment Grant. Child Development Center, UCI, Irvine, CA.

Pfiffner, LJ, & Barkley, RA (1990). Classroom management methods. In RA Barkley (Ed.), Attention deficit hyperactivity disorder: A handbook for diagnosis and treatment. NY: Guilford.

Pfiffner, LJ, O'Leary, SG., Rosen, LA, & Sanderson, WC. (1985). A comparison of the effects of continuous and intermittent response cost and reprimands in the classroom. J Clin Child Psychol, 14, 348-352.

Pfiffner, LJ, Rosen, LA, & O'Leary, SG (1985). The efficacy of an all-positive approach to classroom management. J Applied Behav Anal, 18, 257-261.

PGARD (1990). Submission to the US Department of Education. Notice of Inquiry on ADD.

Rapoport, JL, Buchsbaum, M, Zahn, TP, Weingartner, H, Ludlow, C, & Mikkelsen, EJ (1978). Detroamphetamine: cognitive and behavioral effects on normal prepubertal boys. Science, 199, 560-563.

Rapport, MD, Murphy, HA, & Bailey, JS (1982). Ritalin vs. response cost in the control of hyperactive children: A within- subject comparison. J Applied Behav Anal, 15, 205-216.

Roberts, MA (1990). A behavioral observation method for differenciating hyperactive and aggressive boys. J Abnorl Child Psychol, 18(2), 131-142.

Roberts, MA, Milich, R, Loney, J (1984). Structured observation of academic and play settings (SOAPS). Unpublished Manuscript.

Rosen, LA, O'Leary, SG, Joyce, SA, Conway, G, Pfiffner, LJ (1984). The importance of prudent negative consequences for maintaining the appropriate beahvior of hyperactive students. J Abnor Child Psychol, 12(4), 581-604.

Satterfield, JH, Cantwell, DP, & Satterfield, B (1979). Multimodality treatment: A one-year follow-up of 84 hyperactive boys. Arch Gen Psychiat, 36, 965-974.

Satterfield, JH, Satterfield, BT, & Cantwell, DP (1980). Multimodality treatment. Arch Gen Psychiat, 37, 915-919.

Satterfield, JH, Satterfield, BT, & Cantwell, DP (1981). Three-year multimodality treatment study of 100 hyperactive boys. J Pediat, 98, 650-655.

Satterfield, JH, Satterfield, BT, & Schell, AM (1987). Therapeutic interventions to prevent delinquency in hyperactive boys. J Amer Acad Child Adoles Psychiat, 26, 56-64.

Sergeant, J. (1988). RDC for attention/hyperactivity disorder. In L.M. Bloomingdale and J. Sergeant (eds.), Attention deficit disorder: Criteria, cognition, intervention, (pp. 1-8). NY:Pergamon.

Shaywitz, SE, & Shaywitz, BE (1988). Attention deficit disorder: Current perspectives. In JF Kavanagh & TJ Truss Learning Disabilities: Proceed Natl Conf. Parkton, MD: York.

Silver, LB (1990). Attention deficit-hyperactivity disorder: Is it a learning disability or a related disorder? Journal of Learning Disabilities, 23, 394-397.

Silver, LB (1992). Attention deficit-hyperactivity disorder: A clinical guide to diagnosis and treatment. Washington, D.C.: American Psychiatric Press, Inc.

Skinner, BF (1948). Walden II. NY: MacMillian.

Skinner, BF (1987). Upon Further Reflection. Englewood Cliffs, NJ: Prentice Hall.

Sleator, E & Pelham, WE (1986). Attention Deficit Disorder. New York: Saunders.

Sprague, RL, Sleator, EK. (1977). Methylphenidate in hyperkinetic children: Differences in dose effects on learning and social behavior. Science, 198, 1274-1276.

Swanson, JM (1988). Discussion: Attention deficit disorder. In J.F. Kavanaugh and T.J. Truss (Eds.), Learning disabilities: Proceedings of the National Conference (pp 532-546). Parkton, Maryland: York Press.

Swanson, JM (1989). Paired-associate learning in the assessment of ADD-H children. In L. Bloomingdale & J Swanson (Eds.), Attention Deficit Disorder IV. New York: Pergamon.

Swanson, JM, Simpson, S, Agler, D, Kotkin, R, Pfiffner, L, Bender, M, Roseneau, C, Mayfield, K, Ferrari, L, Holcombe, L, Prince, D, Mordkin, M, Elliot, J, Miura, S, Shea, C, Bonforte, S, Youpa, D, Phillips, L, Nash, L, McBurnett, K, Lerner, M, Robinbson, T, Levin, M, Baren, M, Cantwell, D (1990). UCI-OCDE school-based treatment program for children with ADHD/ODD. In CN Stefanis et al (Eds.), Psychiatry: A world perspective—Vol. 1. NY: Elsevier Science.

Swanson, JM, Cantwell, D, Lerner, M, McBurnett, K, & Hanna, G (1991). Effects of stimulant medication on learning in children with ADHD. J Learn Dis, 24, 219-255.

Swanson, JM, Cantwell, D, Lerner, M, McBurnett, K, Pfiffner, L, & Kotkin, R (1992). Treatment of ADHD: beyond medication. Beyond Behavior, 4, 13-22.

Swanson, JM & Kinsbourne, M (1978). Should you use stimulants to treat the hyperactive child? Modern Medicine, 46, 71-80.

Swanson, JM, Nolan, W, & Pelham, WE (1982). SNAP rating scale. Educational Resources in Education (ERIC).

Swanson, JM, Shea, C, McBurnett, K, Potkin, SG, Fiore, C, & Crinella, F (1990). Attention and hyperactivity. In JT Enns (Ed), The Development of Attention: Research and Theory, 383-403. North Holland: Elsevier Science Publishers.

Swanson, JM et al (1983). Methylphenidate (Ritalin) given with or before breakfast: Part 1. Behavioral, cognitive, and electrophysiological effects. <u>Pediatrics</u>, <u>61</u>, 21-29.

Szatmari, P, Offord, DR, & Boyle, MH (1989). Ontario Child health study: Prevalence of attention deficit disorder with hyperactivity. <u>J Child Psychol Psychiat</u>, <u>30</u>, 219-230.

Turkewitz, H, O'Leary, KD, & Ironsmith, M (1975). Generalization and maintenance of appropriate behavior through self-control. <u>J Conslt Clinic Psychol</u>, <u>43</u>, 577-583.

Thomas, DR, Becker, WC, & Armstrong, M (1968). Production and elimination of disruptive behavior by systemactically varying teacher's behavior. <u>J Applied Behav Anal</u>, <u>1</u>, 35-43.

Ullman, RK, Sleator, EK, & Sprague, RL (1985). A change of mind: The Conners abbreviated rating scales reconsidered. <u>J Abnormal Child Psychol</u>, <u>13</u>(4), 553-565.

Van Houten, R, Nau, PA, MacKenzie-Keating, SE, Sameoto, D, & Colavecchia, B (1982). An analysis of some variables influencing the effectiveness of reprimands. <u>J Applied Behav Anal</u>, <u>15</u>, 65-83
.

Walker, HM & Buckley, NK (1972). Programming generalization and maintenance of treatment effects across time and across settings. <u>J Applied Behav Anal</u>, <u>5</u>, 209-224.

Wender, PH (1971). <u>Minimal Brain Disfunction in Children</u>. NY: Wiley.

Witt, JC (1986). Teachers' resistance to the use of school-based interventions. <u>J School Psychol</u>, <u>24</u>, 37-44.

APPENDIX A

RESPONSE TO THE ADD NOTICE OF INQUIRY
BY THE PROFESSIONAL GROUP FOR ADD AND
RELATED DISORDERS (PGARD)

(Executive Summary)

This response to the Notice of Inquiry is submitted by the Professional Group for ADD and Related Disorders (PGARD), which consists of psychologists, psychiatrists, pediatricians, educators, and social workers who have made a career commitment to investigate Attention Deficit Disorder (ADD). This executive summary is based on detailed responses to each of the twelve questions [(a) through (l)] of the Notice.

146

(a) Are children with attention deficit disorder, who by reason thereof require special education and related services, currently being excluded from special education programs conducted under part B? If so, what is the extent of and what are the reasons for such exclusion?

The members of PGARD estimated that during the 1987-1988 school year, approximately 300,000 children with ADD who required special education services were being excluded from programs conducted under part B of the Education for the Handicapped Act (EHA). Since the recent EHA amendments of 1990 did not change the statues with respect to ADD, the current provisions of the Individuals with Disabilities Education Act (IDEA) are assumed to still exclude the same percentage of children with ADD due to the following reasons: (1) Congress has not acted to list specifically the primary characteristics and educational impact of ADD under categories of handicapping conditions in the EHA/IDEA, and (2) ambiguous interpretations by the Department of Education (DOE) and by State and local school authorities as to whether ADD **alone** is sufficient to make a child eligible for special educational services when this condition adversely affects educational performance.

The Eleventh Annual Report to Congress on the Implementation of the Education for the Handicapped Act estimated that in 1987-1988 approximately 40 million students (ages 6 to 21 years) were attending public schools in the United States. It has been estimated that 5% of this population, or about 2 million children, have ADD. The detailed responses to this Notice suggest that (1) approximately 50% of these children with ADD do not require special education services but instead could be well-served by modification to standard techniques of instruction by personnel in regular classrooms; (2) that approximately 35% of the children with ADD require special education services which could be provided through resource programs and therefore they should be able to receive a significant proportion of their instruction in regular classrooms; (3) that only a small minority of the population of children with ADD (about 15%) require special education services which are provided in self-contained special education classrooms.

Based on this analysis, the members of PGARD estimated that, of the approximately 1 million children with ADD who require special education services, about 30% are being excluded from programs and services offered under part B of the EHA/IDEA. It was suggested that most of the excluded ADD children are those who require special education services which could be provided in resource classrooms (or regular classrooms), and that most of the ADD children who require placement in self-contained classrooms are already in such placements because they have coexisting problems which make them eligible under existing categories of the EHA/IDEA.

(b) To what extent are children with attention deficit disorder, who by reason thereof require special education and related services, currently being identified within existing disability categories in part B, such as "other health impaired," "seriously emotionally disturbed," or "specific learning disability?"

Based on data from the Eleventh Annual Report to Congress on the Implementation of the EHA, it was estimated that in 1987-1988 approximately 700,000 children with ADD were receiving special education services under part B of the EHA/IDEA. Some of these children were clearly eligible to receive services because of coexisting disabilities which qualified them under established EHA/IDEA categories [e.g., Specific Learning Disability (SLD), Seriously Emotionally Disturbed (SED), Other Health Impaired (OHI), and Mental Retardation (MR)]. Others children with ADD alone (and thus not technically meeting the eligibility criteria for existing categories such as SLD, SED, OHI, or MR) were assumed to have been inaccurately labeled but nevertheless placed in programs conducted under part B of the EHA/IDEA.

On the basis of the limited information available, it was estimated that in 1987-1988 the following numbers of ADD children were receiving services within four existing categories of the EHA/IDEA: about 575,000 ADD children in the SLD category, about 100,000 ADD children in the SED category, about 5,000 ADD children in the OHI category, and about 20,000 ADD children in the MR category.

The members of PGARD expressed concern that the services provided within the existing categories of the EHA/IDEA are unlikely to address the specific ADD-related problems of children with ADD. Thus, changes in the types of services provided under part B of the EHA/IDEA were recommended to provide more appropriate special education services to many of the 700,000 ADD children already in existing programs conducted under part B of the EHA/IDEA.

(c) Do children with attention deficit disorder have unique characteristics that are not reflected in the existing disability categories in part B? If so, to what extent do these unique characteristics require separate evaluation criteria, special preparation for instructional and support personnel, and distinct educational programs and services?

A review of the literature indicated that ADD children do have distinctive characteristics, not reflected in currently recognized disability categories of the EHA/IDEA, which relate to the basic operations of orienting, focusing and maintaining attention. Even though these characteristics do require separate evaluation criteria, preparation of instructional material, training of support personnel, and distinct educational services, these ADD-specific components could be provided with reasonable modifications to the existing array of services provided under part B of the EHA/IDEA.

ADD is characterized by developmentally inappropriate inattention, and in many cases impulsivity and overactivity. The manifestation of ADD have early onset and are chronic, so transient episodes of inattention, impulsivity, or hyperactivity are not accepted as characteristics of ADD. The distinctive characteristics of ADD are unique on technical grounds because nowhere within the EHA/IDEA are the ADD-specific characteristics of inattention, impulsivity, or hyperactivity listed as characteristics of any existing category of disability (e.g., as characteristics of SLD or SED). Furthermore, specific characteristics considered to be essential to qualify under existing categories are not present in some ADD children. For example, in the EHA definition of SLD, it is specifically stated that children must have a disorder in one or more of the basic psychological processes involved in under-standing or in using language", but most ADD children do not have language deficits. In the EHA/IDEA definition of SED, the criteria have been interpreted to include internalizing disorders such as depression, anxiety, and schizophrenia and to exclude externalizing disorders such as conduct disorder (CD), oppositional defiant disorder (ODD) on the basis of social maladjustment. Most ADD children do not have coexistent psychiatric disorders associated with emotional distress (eg., as in affective disorder or anxiety disorder) or qualitatively abnormal cognitive or social abilities (eg., as in schizophrenia). Only those ADD children with coexistent language disorders or emotional disorders meet these inclusion criteria for SLD and SED, so the children who manifest only the specific characteristics of ADD are not covered by the existing SLD or SED categories (Bellamy, 1987).

Whether children affected solely with ADD should qualify for special education under the existing OHI category is unclear, due to ambiguous interpretations by the DOE of this question (Bellamy, 1989).

149

(d) What educational programs and/or services are school districts currently providing to children diagnosed as having attention deficit disorder, either in special education programs conducted under part B or in general education programs?

The literature reviewed indicated that very few school systems are currently providing specific educational services for ADD children. A few do, prompted in part by the realization of the adverse impact of ADD on educational performance and in part by directives from the Office of Civil Rights and the courts under section 504 of the Rehabilitation Act to provide supplementary services for ADD children in education settings. However, it is clear that across the country services for children with ADD are being provided in a patchwork rather than an uniform fashion.

Some ADD children receive special education services under the SLD, SED, and MR categories of the EHA/IDEA, but these services are not likely to address specific ADD-related educational problems since these are not the problems which made them eligible for special education services under existing guidelines. In any Individual Education Plan (IEP), the EHA/IDEA compels schools to address those aspects of the condition which qualified the child for special educational services. Consequently, the large numbers of ADD children already in special education do not necessarily receive educational programs or services specifically tailored to their ADD-related problems. Existing services provided for them in the SLD (e.g., language-based skills and tutoring) and SED (e.g., management of social and emotional disturbances) categories are neither optimal nor adequate for addressing ADD-specific educational problems.

To correct this, the members of PGARD recommended that Congress and the DOE recognize ADD, with appropriate restrictions for degree of educational impairment, and make children with ADD eligible for ADD-specific special education services under part B of the EHA/IDEA.

Court cases, including a California Supreme Court decision, and several OCR rulings have established the legal precedent that ADD can be a handicapping condition and therefore children with it are protected against discrimination under Section 504 of the Rehabilitation Act of 1973. The OCR rulings have directed that school districts take corrective action so that children with ADD who are not receiving special education services are identified, evaluated, and if appropriate, provided educational services under Section 504.

(e) How should attention deficit disorder be described operationally for purposes of qualifying a child for special education and related services under part B?

On the basis of extensive review of the literature and broad consultation, the following educational description of ADD has been formulated:

The condition 'attention deficit disorder' refers to a developmental disorder involving one or more of the basic cognitive processes related to orienting, focusing or maintaining **attention**, resulting in a marked degree of inadequate attention to academic and social tasks. The disorder may also include verbal or motor impulsivity and excessive non-task related activities such as fidgeting or restlessness. The inattentive behavior of ADD most commonly has onset in early childhood, remains inappropriate for age, and persists throughout development.

ADD adversely affects educational performance to the extent that a significant discrepancy exists between a child's intellectual ability and that child's productivity with respect to listening, following directions, planning, organizing, or completing academic assignments which require reading, writing, spelling, or mathematical calculations.

Inattentive behaviors, if caused by cultural differences, socioeconomic disadvantage, or lack of adequate exposure to the language of educational instruction, are not evidence of ADD. Inattentive behaviors with acute onset are not evidence of ADD if they arise directly from (1) stressful events associated with family functioning (e.g., parental divorce, or the death of a family member or close friend) or environmental disruption (e.g., a change in residence or school); (2) post-traumatic stress reactions caused by abuse (e.g., physical, psychological, or sexual) or natural disasters; (3) noncompliance due solely to opposition or defiance; (4) frustration resulting from inappropriate tasks beyond intellectual ability or level of achievement skills; or (5) emotional disorders (e.g., anxiety, depression, schizophrenia).

ADD can co-exist with other handicapping conditions (i.e., specific learning disabilities, serious emotional disturbance, or mental retardation).

The following definitions are given for the terms stated above:
1. "a marked degree" means, at a minimum, disproportionate for the child's age as measured by well-standardized and unbiased rating scales or structured interviews which result in functional impairment.
2. "onset in early childhood" means that when a careful developmental history of the child is obtained, it confirms that parents, teachers, or other involved adults have observed the development of the age-inappropriate inattentive behaviors before the age of 7 years. The onset of these persistent inattentive behaviors should not to be confused with the educational manifestations of ADD, because onset of educational impairment may occur at any time in the child's life when school tasks tax the child's underlying attentional deficit.

151

(f) What criteria should be included in the definition to qualify children with attention deficit disorder whose disability is comparable in severity to other children with disabilities currently determined to be eligible for special education and related services under part B?

As set forth in the proposed educational definition of ADD, the criteria for ADD are quite comparable to those used to determine eligibility for other disabilities currently recognized in part B of the EHA/IDEA. The proposed ADD definition is based on a two-tier framework: (1) first, it must be confirmed that the child has the ADD disorder based on specific criteria which include cardinal characteristics, early onset, chronic duration, and exclusion conditions; (2) second, it must be determined that the educational manifestation of ADD (which may have an onset at any point in the ADD child's life) is severe enough to have an adverse impact on educational performance.

The following operational criteria for qualifying an ADD child for special education services are in keeping with the intent and scope of EHA to address the educational needs of children with disabilities: ADD adversely affects educational performance to the extent that a significant discrepancy exists between a child's intellectual ability and that child's educational productivity with respect to listening, following directions, planning, organizing or completing academic assignments that require reading, writing, spelling or mathematical calculations.

(g) What specific manifestations of attention deficit disorder, if any, should be included in the definition?

As noted in the definition presented in response to question (e), the specific manifestations of ADD include impairments in the ability to orient, focus and maintain attention to educational and social tasks. A two-tier assessment and evaluation strategy was presented in response to question (j) which was designed to maintain specificity (tier 1) and objectivity (tier 2). The tier 2 evaluation focuses on the educational manifestations of ADD.

152

(h) Should the definition include references to characteristics or circumstances that produce transient inattentive behaviors that, in and of themselves, would not make a child eligible for special education and related services under the definition of attention deficit disorder?

The proposed educational definition of ADD excludes inattention resulting solely from reactions to emotional distress or environmental stresses, which would not alone be evidence for ADD or make a child eligible for special education and related services. Moreover, inattentive behaviors attributed to cultural differences, socioeconomic disadvantages, or lack of adequate exposure to the language of educational instruction, are not evidence of ADD.

(i) Should the definition address the concurrence of attention deficit disorder with other disabilities, such as specific learning disabilities or serious emotional disturbance, and if so addressed, how should this be accomplished?

The proposed definition addresses the occurrence of ADD with other disabilities included in IDEA part B by indicating that eligibility would be evaluated under all appropriate categories.

(j) Should guidelines be provided to State and local educational agencies regarding their obligation to conduct an evaluation of a child suspected of having attention deficit disorder? If so, how should these guidelines be described?

Unambiguous and standardized guidelines should be provided to state and local agencies in place of the piecemeal practices which are now applied inconsistently for evaluation of ADD children. The proposed educational definition of ADD, presented in response to question (e) of the Notice, provides the basis for standardized assessment of ADD. A two-tiered system of evaluation was proposed, involving the following: (1) documentation of the history and academic manifestations of ADD through reports of those most familiar with the child (e.g., parents and regular education teachers), and (2) objective assessment of the adverse impact of ADD on educational performance including observations in the classroom, comparison with peers, academic productivity, information on other disorders, and trial interventions.

153

(k) Who should be authorized to conduct an assessment of a child having or suspected of having attention deficit disorder, and should the assessment be conducted by more than one individual (such as a teacher and a psychologist)?

Instructional and support personnel who currently evaluate children for eligibility under existing categories of the EHA/IDEA could readily be trained to conduct the proposed Tier 1 assessment of the cardinal features of ADD and the proposed Tier 2 evaluation of its educational impact. To prepare existing and future staff to perform assessments of ADD children, training will be required throughout the professional education process, including instruction about ADD during training for certification and on in continuing education for already certified regular and special education teachers.

(l) What provisions should be included in the definition, and what additional steps, if any, not currently required by the regulations implementing part B, should be included to ensure that children who are from racial, ethnic, and linguistic minorities are not misclassified under this definition?

The members of PGARD recognize that racial, ethnic, and linguistic minorities are over-represented in existing categories of special education. In preparation for the response to this question of the Notice, members of the civil rights and disabilities communities were consulted in an effort to address this problem. Opinions and advice was sought and received from minority psychologists and psychiatrists who work with ADD children were.

Although ADD appears to occur with uniform prevalence among all racial, ethnic and linguistic groups, safeguards are required to protect minority children from being misclassified and over identified under any definition of the EHA/IDEA. The basic safeguards of our approach would include: (1) involving in the evaluation team at least one member of the child's minority who is knowledgeable regarding potential bias; (2) comparing the minority child being evaluated with children of similar minority status; (3) addressing the manifestations of the conditions and circumstances noted above which alone would not be evidence of ADD. In general, it was recommended that to the extent possible, evaluation teams should strive to use broad-based assessment procedures and instruments which minimize biases against minority children, are sensitive to cultural nuances of different ethnic groups, take into consideration the level of the child's acculturation, and are conducted in the child's primary language.

The members of PGARD recommend that Congress and the Department of Education do the following: (1) acknowledge that certain children with ADD be considered "children with disabilities" under part B of IDEA **solely** on the basis of the existence of this disorder in situations where ADD adversely affects educational performance, (2) provide consistent, just and nondiscriminatory directives to States for recognizing, assessing and educating ADD children, and (3) provide adequate resources for the appropriate training of regular and special education teachers and other professionals in evaluating and providing services.

154

The members of PGARD believe that these responses and recommendations satisfactorily address the issues raised in the Notice of Inquiry concerning ADD. The responses have been based on established scientific findings and expert professional opinion from professionals in education, child psychology, child psychiatry, pediatrics, child neurology, and social work. This response to the Notice is offered to help Congress and the DOE determine how to best to address the educational needs of ADD children.

Submitted for the membership by the officers of PGARD:

Lewis Bloomingdale, M.D.
Associate Clinical Professor of Psychiatry
New York Medical College
President, PGARD

James M. Swanson, Ph.D.
Professor of Pediatrics, Psychiatry, and Social Science
University of California, Irvine
President-Elect, PGARD

Russell A. Barkley, Ph.D.
Professor of Psychiatry and Neurology
University of Massachusetts Medical Center
Secretary, PGARD

James Satterfield, M.D.
National Center for the Study of Hyperactive Children
Treasurer, PGARD

APPENDIX B

Congressional Testimony:
Letter to Representative Bartlett

March 5, 1990

The Honorable Steve Bartlett, M.C.
Committee on Education and Labor
1113 Longworth House
Washington, D.C. 20515

Dear Congressman Bartlett:

Thank you for the opportunity to testify before the Education and Labor Committee last week during the hearings on amendments to PL 94-142. I appreciate the opportunity to address issues about Attention Deficit Disorder (DSM III, 1980) or Attention Deficit-Hyperactivity Disorder (DSM IIIR, 1987). In the next revision of the Diagnostic and Statistical Manual (DSM IV, 1992), it is likely that both of these labels (ADD and ADHD) will be used to specify variants of the disorder (Garfinkel, 1990), so I will use the combined label ADD/ADHD.

After the testimony on ADD/ADHD, you had several questions, and based on the verbal answers, you requested written information about several issues:

(1) Does ADD/ADHD exist as a recognizable disorder with a high degree of agreement among professionals?

(2) What is the prevalence of ADD/ADHD?

(3) Are ADD/ADHD children being identified and served under current law?

(4) If ADD/ADHD were added to PL 94-142 and specified as a handicapping condition, what type and range of services would the public schools be asked to provide?

This letter provides answers to your questions on behalf of the Bloomingdale Professional Group for Attention and Related Disorders (PGARD), a small society composed of about 40 scientists and clinicians who specialize in the evaluation and treatment of ADD/ADHD. This multidisciplinary society has members from five professions (psychology, psychiatry, pediatrics, neurology and education) involved in the assessment and treatment of ADD/ADHD. The PGARD society was founded by Lewis Bloomingdale, M.D. in 1980, and it has met annually for the past 10 years. For the past five years, I have acted as the scientific program chairman, and under our editorship (Swanson and Bloomingdale), the PGARD society publishes scholarly monographs on critical issues about ADD/ADHD.

The Bloomingdale PGARD society has a steering committee which is composed of eminent representatives from the United States and Europe. The four disciplines are represented by psychologist Keith Conners, Ph.D., Duke University; psychiatrist Dennis Cantwell, M.D., University of California, Los Angeles; pediatrician Sally Shaywitz, M.D., and neurologist Bennett Shaywitz, M.D., Yale University; educator Steve Forness, Ed.D., University of California, Los Angeles. Other members of the steering committee include individuals from the United States (psychologist William Pelham, Ph.D., University of Pittsburgh; psychiatrist James Satterfield, M.D., National Center for Hyperactivity), Canada (psychologist Virginia Douglas, Ph.D., McGill University) and from abroad (psychiatrist Eric Taylor, M.D., Institute for Psychiatry, London; psychologist Joseph Sergeant, Ph.D., University of Amsterdam).

Recently, the Bloomingdale PGARD society has agreed to act as the professional advisory group to a national coalition of parent groups, the Attention Deficit Disorder Association (ADDA). Nancy Cornish and other officers of this parent organization prompted me to offer testimony to your Committee as a representative of professionals who specialize in the investigation and treatment of ADD/ADHD children.

As you requested after my testimony, I am providing written information on each of your four questions:

(1) Does ADD/ADHD exist as a recognizable disorder with a high degree of agreement among professionals?

Over the past 10 years, an international research effort has clearly defined the ADD/ADHD syndrome. The core features of the disorder fall into two categories — inattention and impulsivity/hyperactivity. These cognitive and motor deficits in ADD/ADHD are not specifically related to "the basic psychological processes involved in understanding and using language" or to "severe emotional disturbance", so ADD/ADHD alone is not considered to be a learning disability or an emotional disability according to the LD or SED definitions applied to determine eligibility for services under PL 94-142.

However, the ADD/ADHD symptoms themselves create severe problems for the affected child in the classroom (in interactions with the teacher) and outside the classroom (in interactions with peers). A large literature has demonstrated that ADD/ADHD children create extreme disruption in the standard classroom (eg, Whalen and Henker, 1980; Atkins et al, 1986), and thus their deficit may detract from the educational experience of others as well as themselves.

Diagnostic terms for the ADD/ADHD syndrome have changed frequently, but the changes have been to refine the definition of ADD/ADHD, not to question its existence as a separate disorder. Over the past 10 years, two formulations have been proposed in the American Psychiatric Association's Diagnostic and Statistical Manual (DSM): (a) in DSM III (1980), two forms of the disorder were recognized and labeled Attention Deficit Disorder with (ADDH) or without (ADD) hyperactivity; (b) in DSM IIIR (1987), a single form of the disorder was recognized and labeled Attention Deficit Hyperactivity Disorder (ADHD). These changes reflect scientific honesty in a serious attempt to describe a complex disorder, not the fruitless pursuit of a nonexistent disorder (Gittleman Klein, 1988).

When specific criteria are used, different forms of ADD/ADHD can be reliably diagnosed. Recent evidence comes from an important cross-cultural study conducted in the United States (by Judith Rapaport, M.D. from NIMH in Washington, D.C.) and in the United Kingdom (by Eric Taylor, M.D. from the Institute of Psychiatry in London). [This study is particularly interesting, because it was once thought that ADD/ADHD was 20 times more prevalent in the USA than in the UK, but this view was based on methodological differences in the two countries and has been refuted (Taylor et al, 1990).] In the proceedings of the 5th Bloomingdale PGARD meeting, <u>Attention Deficit Disorder: Criteria, Cognition, Intervention</u>, edited by Bloomingdale and Sergeant (1988), Taylor (p 145) summarized the results of the study in which the different USA and UK definitions of the disorder were specified and diagnosed. When the stated diagnostic rules were followed, Taylor reported the following:

> "...even in a group in whom diagnostic distinctions
> are likely to be uncertain and vexatious... it is
> encouraging to find a solid agreement... comparable
> with or better than that found in studies of more
> securely differentiated conditions." Even in the
> worst case, the data showed "...perfect agreement
> on better than 80% of the cases".

The reliability of the diagnosis of ADD/ADHD has been described in several articles published in reputable journals [eg., Cantwell (1980 and 1983), Shaywitz et al (1986), Werry (1989) and Prendergast et al (1988)]. Furthermore, the validity of the ADD/ADHD diagnosis has been confirmed by the established methods of syndrome validation which have been formulated over the years [eg., by follow-up studies which document that adult outcomes for ADD/ADHD individuals differ from outcomes for other children based on the natural history of the disorder (Satterfield et al, 1982; Weiss et al, 1979; Mannuzza et al, 1988) and by physiological studies which show that ADD/ADHD children differ from others based on topographical patterns of brain activation (Lou et al, 1984; Satterfield et al, 1988)]. Much of the recent information on reliability and validity of diagnosis of ADD/ADHD has been summarized for the scientific and clinical community in the book by Bloomingdale and Sergeant (1988), published as a monograph supplement to the Journal of Child Psychology and Psychiatry, the official publication of the international learned society, the Association for Child Psychology and Psychiatry. I am enclosing a copy of this reference book for the Committee's use in its deliberations about revisions of PL 94-142.

I was not present for the initial testimony before your Committee, but you indicated that my testimony conflicted with prior testimony. During the question period, you indicated that in prior testimony it had been asserted that the ADD/ADHD disorder either does not exist separate from other disorders or that the consensus among professionals was so low that ADD/ADHD cannot be diagnosed reliably. This view has been expressed in the past as a hypothesis by reputable scientists (eg., Rutter et al, 1970; Shaffer, 1980) and clinicians (eg, Levine et al, 1980) but the last decade of intensive investigation has refuted this notion (eg, see Gittleman Klein, 1988; Taylor et al, 1990; Shaywitz and Shaywitz, 1988).

Still, popular journalists (eg, Schrag and Divoky, 1975; Kohn, 1989) and biased fringe groups (eg., the Church of Scientology and its Citizens Committee on Human Rights, 1987) have continued to make this claim, or even the more stringent claim that ADD/ADHD symptoms represent normal variants of behavior that just are not tolerated by some parents or schools. Reputable clinicians who specialize in the assessment and treatment of this disorder (eg, see Shaywitz and Shaywitz, 1988), groups of scientists who investigate this disorder (eg., see Bloomingdale and Sergeant, 1988; Bloomingdale and Swanson, 1989), and a large number of parents who deal with the day-to-day realities of the disorder (eg, ADDA and CHADD), attest to the existence of the disorder.

The Bloomingdale PGARD group is concerned that the incorrect view that ADD/ADHD does not exist as a separate disorder, and the outdated view that it cannot be diagnosed reliably, are being presented unchallenged in testimony to your Committee. We urge your Committee not to accept this view as an accurate description of the state of nature. To do so would be inconsistent with the status of ADD/ADHD given by your own scientific advisors in the 1987 report to Congress from the Interagency Committee on Learning Disabilities. The Interagency Report to Congress was based in part on the proceedings of the National Conference on Learning Disabilities (Kavanaugh and Truss, 1988), wherein Shaywitz and Shaywitz (1988) present a massive (over 150 pages) up-to-date and scholarly review of the ADD/ADHD area. You probably already have a copy of this reference book, but I am enclosing another copy so it will be handy for the Committee to consult for additional details about ADD/ADHD.

The Interagency Committee offered clear support for the existence of ADD/ADHD as a disorder separate from LD. The place that this is most clearly stated is in the discussion of the conference proceedings and the implications for revisions in the definition of learning disabilities (Kavanaugh and Truss, 1988, pp 549-551). The Interagency Committee recommended that specific reference to ADD/ADHD "...should be added to the definition" and that this revised definition "...should be considered ... for use in future legislation" (Kavanaugh and Truss, 1988, p 550).

The assertion that ADD/ADHD does not exist as a separate disorder or that it cannot be diagnosed reliably is based on the notion that its symptoms may be byproducts of other disorders and that the ADD/ADHD symptoms do not exist on their own to define a separate disorder. In the past, inattention and overactivity have been described as byproducts of emotional and conduct disorders (Rutter et al, 1970; Shaffer, 1980), learning disabilities (Silver, 1980), depression (Brumback and Weinberg, 1977), or general stress in childhood (Levine et al, 1980). The contention that this makes ADD/ADHD unrecognizable as a separate disorder represents a strong point of view that has been addressed as a legitimate research question and has been thoroughly discussed in the literature (see Gittleman Klein, 1988 or Taylor, 1988; Taylor et al, 1990). In each case the existence of ADD/ADHD as a separate syndrome has been established in the arena of scientific investigation [eg, as described by Hinshaw (1986) about conduct disorder, Shaywitz and Shaywitz (1986) about learning disabilities, and Carlson and Cantwell (1980) about depression].

Studies of comorbidity clearly indicate that the ADD/ADHD disorder occurs concurrently with other emotional or learning disorders but that this mixed form of the disorder does not represent the majority of ADD/ADHD cases. In some cases, the presence of another disorder provides exclusion criteria which may override an ADD/ADHD diagnosis based solely on symptom presence. For example, an acute emotional episode of depression or anxiety is likely to produce symptoms of inattention or overactivity in a child (Cantwell and Carlson, 1983), but a diagnosis of ADD/ADHD would not be warranted, since the criteria for onset (before age 6) and temporal course (presence across developmental stages starting in preschool) would not be met. Presence of other disorders [eg, such as conduct disorder (CD) or learning disability (LD)] usually does not preclude a diagnosis of ADD/ADHD. In fact, when rigorous definitions are used, CD may be diagnosed in 40% or more of the ADD/ADHD cases (Taylor et al, 1990), and LD may occur in 10% of the ADD/ADHD cases.

Recognition of ADD/ADHD is not a simple matter. The attentional processes which underlie the disorder usually do not produce a deficit in a single area that is invariant across conditions and time. Variability across situations is expected (Garfinkel, 1990). For example, an ADD/ADHD child may manifest extreme problems in a reading group, but in 1 to 1 interactions with the teacher the same child may be an excellent reader. Or, the ADD/ADHD child may manifest severe symptoms in everyday interactions in the home and school, but show no observable signs of ADD/ADHD during the first visit to the doctor's office (Sleator et al, 1981). Thus, even though pervasiveness of symptoms (ie, their appearance in more than one setting) should be required for reliable diagnosis, the failure of ADD/ADHD symptoms to occur in all situations or on every occasion does not preclude making the diagnosis.

These factors — multiple forms of ADD/ADHD, exclusion criteria, and variability of expression of symptoms — suggest that the ADD/ADHD disorder is complicated enough to require a specialist to make a reliable diagnosis (Taylor et al, 1990; Werry, 1989). The Bloomingdale PGARD group appreciates the Committee's willingness to consider the opinions of experts who specialize in the assessment of ADD/ADHD on the issues of the existence, reliability and validity of this diagnostic category.

Thus, a balanced answer to your first question must acknowledge that there are some disagreements among professionals about the diagnosis of ADD/ADHD but an extensive literature makes it clear that most valid disagreements are about the form of the ADHD disorder, not about its existence as a separate disorder. If a rigorous definition is followed, the ADD/ ADHD disorder can be diagnosed in a reliable and valid way.

(2) What is the prevalence of ADHD?

A conservative estimate of the prevalence of the ADD/ADHD disorder is under 2% of the elementary school-aged population (Taylor et al, 1990), but standard estimates are higher (usually 3% to 5%). Any estimate of prevalence depends upon the criteria of pervasiveness (ie, that symptoms appear in several different settings) and severity (ie, that the symptoms are extreme compared to norms). Clinical judgment of severity and pervasiveness should be based on the criteria of functional impairment (Cantwell, 1980; Taylor et al, 1990) and experienced clinicians use structured interviews to filter parent and teacher reports of symptoms to ensure that low adult tolerance for normal childhood behavior does not result in a categorical diagnosis solely on symptom counts derived from parent and teacher ratings.

The prevalence of ADD as defined by DSM III (1980) criteria may be extremely high (15% to 20%). However, this is not the intent expressed in the DSM III manual, which estimated the prevalence of ADD to be about 3%. DSM III (1980) criteria put an emphasis on one source (the teacher) and used severity criteria (number of symptoms) based on a committee decision rather than a controlled field trial. Thus, strict application of DSM criteria for ADD identifies "attention problems" as well as "attention disorders" - see Shaywitz and Shaywitz (1988), Kavanaugh and Truss (1988), and Taylor et al (1990). Following the revision of DSM III criteria, August and Garfinkel (1989) provided an estimate of about 9% for the prevalence of the DSM IIIR (1987) diagnosis of ADHD, but this too was based on a single source (teacher ratings). The most up-to-date diagnostic criteria for ADD/ADHD are provided by Bloomingdale and Sergeant (1988), and by Taylor et al (1990). Both sets require confirmation of symptoms by one source and a level of severity that is sufficient to ensure functional impairment. The proposed DSM IV criteria (Garfinkel, 1990) also require more than one source and impose strict severity criteria (4 out of 5 inattention symptoms and 6 out of 9 hyperactivity/ impulsivity symptoms) for making a diagnosis of ADHD. Criteria for making a diagnosis of ADD without hyperactivity have been made stricter by requiring 3 out of 4 additional inattention symptoms.

When multiple sources are required to confirm a diagnosis and strict severity criteria are imposed, then the prevalence of ADD/ADHD is under 2% (Lambert, 1978,; Taylor et al, 1990). This is not a new approach. It has been assumed and accepted by some all along (eg, see Swanson, 1988) that only 2% of the population or about one tenth of the subgroup of children with attention problems should be diagnosed with a specific attention disorder that requires an intensive treatment program. Nonspecific inattention and overactivity symptoms may be associated with primary behavioral disorders (or other forms of social maladjustment) or emotional disorders (Taylor et al, 1990), but the temporal pattern of these conditions may be interpreted as exclusion criteria for a diagnosis of ADD/ADHD (Swanson et al, 1990).

Thus, to answer your second question, a conservative estimate of prevalence (2%) is proposed, based on strict requirements for severity and pervasiveness. This is in the face of some dissent for a higher estimate, but the draft criteria for the forthcoming DSM IV revision require this conservative approach (Garfinkel, 1990).

(3) Under the current version of PL 94-142 are ADHD children being recognized and served in the public schools?

Since PL 94-142 does not specify ADD/ADHD as a handicapping condition, special services are difficult to obtain in a public school setting. Some ADD/ADHD children who have multiple diagnoses may qualify based on the presence of a learning disability (LD) or a serious emotional disturbance (SED), which are specified as handicapping conditions in PL 94-142. However, as previously reviewed, these overlaps are smaller than once assumed:

(a) Current estimates suggest that approximately 10% of all ADD/ ADHD children may qualify for the LD diagnosis based on IQ-achievement test discrepancy scores (Halperin et al, 1984; Shaywitz and Shaywitz, 1988; Forness et al, 1990).

(b) Even though 25% to 45% of all ADD/ADHD children may meet some criteria for a concurrent diagnosis of conduct disorder [eg, in DSM IIIR criteria either a diagnosis of Oppositional Defiant Disorder (ODD) or Conduct Disorder (CD)], only a small proportion of these children may be judged to have a serious emotional disturbance and qualify for special services based on the PL 94-142 definition of SED.

Forness and Kavale (1989) outlined how the PL 94-142 criteria for LD and SED were linked to subtypes of learning disabilities and to "equivalent" DSM III psychiatric diagnoses. According to their analysis, current SED criteria do match up with some psychiatric diagnoses (eg., schizophrenia, depression, etc.) but not with the ADD/ADHD diagnosis. Usually, the mixed diagnosis of ADD/ADHD and CD is considered to represent "social maladjustment" which makes a child ineligible for special education under the current SED guidelines. Furthermore, their analysis suggests that if strict LD criteria were imposed, then many LD-labeled children would not meet PL 94-142 guidelines for a LD classification.

Thus, only a few ADD children are already eligible for services under PL 94-142 (ie, the mixed cases of ADD/ADHD plus LD and ADD/ADHD plus extreme CD). A large majority of all children with diagnoses of ADD/ADHD would be excluded by rigorous application of the current guidelines. These ADD/ADHD children have significant academic problems but according to the letter of the law they do not officially qualify for special services under the current version of PL 94-142 since their problems are not specifically tied to language processing problems or to serious emotional disturbances.

However, this does not mean that these ADD/ADHD children do not obtain services through PL 94-142. When there is a legitimate need, enterprising and persistent parents try to find a way that the need can be met. Reports in the literature suggest that this has resulted in the tactical misuse of the LD label. According to the analysis by Forness and Kavale (1989), about 30% of the 1.8 million LD-labeled children in special education placements under the current PL 94-142 guidelines (or about 600,000 children in 1986) do not have well-defined language processing deficits. Instead, these children have "production deficits" (Weller and Strawser, 1987) and probably have ADHD as the primary diagnosis (Forness and Kavale, 1989, p 295).

The literature suggests that the LD label is often distorted to meet the needs of children in need of special education services and that this is not an isolated occurrence. It is surprising to note that the distortion of the LD label seems to occur for about 2% of the elementary school-aged population, which is equal to the conservative prevalence rate of ADD/ADHD. Shaywitz and Shaywitz (1988, p 402) have pointed out how mislabeling is a serious problem that complicates the scientific investigation of LD: children who are identified as LD for special education placement cannot be used to define a LD group for research purposes, since a significant number of these children with the LD label will actually meet the criteria for ADD/ADHD but not for LD.

Thus, several sources (Weller and Strawser, 1987; Shaywitz and Shaywitz, 1988; Forness and Kavale, 1989) suggest that a significant number of ADD/ADHD children are given the LD label to qualify for special services, even though they do not meet the established criteria for LD. This creates a considerable amount of conflict and frustration for the parents of ADD/ADHD children in the evaluation process necessary to gain access to special services in the public schools.

Even if the mislabeling of ADD/ADHD children, this does not mean that ADD/ADHD children will automatically receive the appropriate interventions when they gain access to the special education benefits. Special programs designed to treat children with LD or SED may not be appropriate for the ADD/ADHD children who do not have learning disabilities or emotional disturbances. In fact, most of the non-LD and non-SED ADD/ADHD children may best be served if specific behavioral interventions are implemented by the regular classroom teacher, with consultation (planning, training and monitoring) by a professional. (This is addressed in the answer to question 4, below).

In some cases, special programs have been designed to provide treatment for ADD/ADHD children in the public school system even though they do not qualify under strict application of the LD or SED guidelines defined by PL 94-142. At the University of California, Irvine, we applied for and received a waiver which allows for treatment based on the ADD/ADHD diagnosis (Swanson, 1988; Swanson et al, 1990), but this is an isolated and special case.

Not all ADD/ADHD children qualify for special education by distorting the LD label. Often, ADD/ADHD children seem to have the ability to perform normally in school, so many are left in regular classrooms without any special help. There, "production deficits" result in poor performance in the usual classroom, and ADD/ADHD children may be exhorted to try harder or admonished because they should "know better". These approaches do not work and in fact may have negative emotional consequences. This may represent one route into more serious antisocial behavior as an adolescent or an adult (Satterfield, 1990).

Thus, the answer to your third question is that some multihandicapped ADD/ADHD children (with concurrent specific learning and serious emotional problems) qualify for special education placement under current definitions of LD and SED in PL 94-142, but in a majority of the cases, distortions of the current LD and SED labels must (and do) occur to obtain these services for ADD/ADHD children. Even when special services are provided, they may not address the specific non-LD and non-SED problems of ADD/ADHD children.

(4) If ADD/ADHD were included as a handicapping condition in PL 94-142, what type and range of services would be appropriate for intervention in the public schools?

At the most basic level, teachers provide a valuable source of information about ADD/ADHD children. They are the sources of information, observations, and data for use by outside teams who assess and treat ADD/ADHD children. This is the case for the large number of children who have attention problems rather than disorders. Thus, teacher training about ADD/ADHD is essential to make teachers aware of the disorder. The costs of screening for early intervention are trivial compared to the costs of delayed recognition and treatment.

When ADD/ADHD is defined by severity and pervasiveness criteria so that the prevalence of the diagnosis is only 2% of the school-aged population, then multimodality treatment is usually required. This includes involvement of a physician (for pharmacological intervention in some but not all cases), the parents (for implementing behavioral program in the home), and the school (for providing altered educational settings). Different ways to provide multimodality treatment have been described [eg, see Satterfield et al (1985), Pelham (1989), and Swanson et al (1990)]. For the sake of relevance to PL 94-142, comments in this letter will be restricted to the area of school intervention for ADD/ADHD children.

Unfortunately, in the United States the educational component has not received the attention that the medical component (ie, treatment with stimulant drugs) has received. As a result, it is likely that nonpharmacological interventions in the school are underused and that interventions based on pharmacological intervention alone are overused in the United States. The current version of PL 94-142, by making educational services difficult to obtain, may have contributed to this biased pattern of intervention.

Systematic interventions in the classroom are required for most ADD/ADHD children. It is likely that usual school-wide discipline systems (eg, programs which result in systematic exclusion from the classroom or suspension from school), even though appropriate for the majority of the elementary school-aged population, are not sufficient for children with ADD/ADHD. ADD/ADHD children respond to punishment as well as to positive consequences, but a contingency management system that provides immediate feedback and powerful rewards is essential for effective intervention. This requires special training and supplementary resources to be implemented in the school setting (Pfiffner and O'Leary, 1990).

Interventions targeted for language based problems (LD programs) or emotional problems (SED programs) are not the specific interventions of choice for ADD/ADHD children. The behaviors of children with ADD/ADHD as a separate disorder are qualitatively different from other children in terms of attentiveness, verbal intrusion and accuracy of academic work (Atkins et al, 1986). Interventions targeting these production deficits are needed. The primary school-based interventions for ADD/ADHD are based on the principles and techniques of behavior modification. The typical way of delivering this type of intervention is for a professional to consult with the teacher who then implements the behavior modification program in the classroom (O'Leary et al, 1976; Pelham, 1977; O'Leary and Pelham, 1978; Barkley, 1981; Pelham and Murphy, 1986; Carlson and Lahey, 1989).

166

The first step of behavioral intervention involves targeting specific problem behaviors which are defined by the symptoms of ADD/ADHD. A consensus (see Barkley, 1981; Pelham and Bender, 1985; Swanson et al, 1990) has developed over the years about a specific set of classroom situations where ADD/ADHD children have difficulty. For example, the functional impairment of most ADD/ADHD children in the classroom may be associated with the following target behaviors:

(a) getting started when the class is directed to work,
(b) staying on task for the length of a standard
classroom period (eg, 30 minutes),
(c) completing assignments when independent work is required,
(d) maintaining classroom deportment when silence and stillness
are required,
(e) interacting appropriately with teaching staff and peers
during classroom activities,
(e) changing activities when the class is instructed to stop
one activity and switch to another.

This list of standard problems can be used to establish a simple token system that operates on an interval schedule [ie, the teacher may give feedback by awarding tokens (points) for appropriate behavior every 30 minutes]. Backup reinforcers (rewards) may be provided at home by the parents or in the school environment, by making natural consequences (privileges) contingent upon an accumulation of tokens. The prudent use of negative consequences, including soft reprimands, response cost, and loss of privileges when appropriately applied reduce the staffing required to establish an effective contingency management program in the classroom (Pfiffner et al, 1987).

Standard daily report systems and home-based reward programs have been based on these techniques. O'Leary (1975), Pfiffner and O'Leary (1990) and Pfiffner and Barkley (1990) have summarized an extensive literature on the use of contingency programs in the classroom. O'Leary et al (1976), Pelham et al (1989) and Swanson et al (1990) describe school-based behavior modification programs that have been implemented in model school programs. Loney et al (1985) present a practical implementation of a simple behavioral program in the regular classroom.

Behavior modification programs are effective to elicit the use of intact abilities which ADD/ADHD children possess but do not use on their own. This approach may not be sufficient for teaching new skills for improving poor peer interaction, which is also a serious problem for most ADD/ADHD children. In some cases, it may be necessary to implement skill training in small groups, based on principles of shaping and using cognitive-behavioral methods. Specific techniques for modeling, coaching, and reinforced practice have been developed (eg., Oden and Asher, 1977) and can be applied effectively in the school setting (see Hazel and Schumaker, 1988). These techniques can be implemented by a psychologist or a behavioral specialist meeting with small groups of students outside the classroom. The direct instructional approach has been recommended for the cognitive teaching of peer interaction skills (Walker, 1988) and has been implemented in a school setting (Swanson et al, 1990).

Clinical experience suggests that these behavioral interventions could be implemented in regular classrooms in about 60% of the diagnosed cases. However, training, monitoring and incentive programs for teachers are essential to ensure that well-designed programs are implemented. Clinical experience suggests that placement in small special classrooms would be required in about 30% of the cases, and placement in a special day class or special school would be required in about 10% of the cases. This corresponds to about the number of ADD/ADHD children that Forness (1989) estimated to be already in special education placement by means of distortions of the LD and SED labels.

The answer to the fourth question is straightforward: specific behavioral techniques exist to provide effective intervention for ADD/ADHD symptoms. These techniques have been applied in regular classrooms, in small special classrooms, and in special schools, but these interventions are not typically provided for ADD/ADHD children in the public schools.

I hope that this letter will answer your questions about ADD/ADHD. On scientific grounds, the Bloomingdale PGARD group strongly recommends the following:

(1) The use of diagnostic terms for handicapping conditions that accurately describe the children who need and are placed in special education programs. "Backdoor" routes into these programs, through tactical misuse of the LD or SED labels, introduce unnecessary and devious factors into an already complicated area.

(2) The use of rigorous definitions and specialized professionals to make categorical diagnoses of ADD/ADHD. The reliance on teacher or parent reports or ratings, without imposing exclusion criteria or requiring severity and pervasiveness conditions to ensure that functional impairment exists, may result in subthreshold attentional problems being identified as a psychiatric disorder and thus inflate the prevalence of ADD/ADHD.

We hope that you agree that the current law has serious problems with respect to ADD/ADHD, and we hope that you will correct these problems with an amendment to PL 94-142. We recommend a straightforward approach as the solution. Since the ADD/ADHD syndrome represents a clinical reality that will not go away, and since a portion of these children already receive services under some other guise, we recommend that ADD/ADHD be recognized as a separate handicapping condition. Given a strict definition of ADD/ADHD to restrict the prevalence to 2%, this may not produce dramatic changes in the number of ADD/ADHD children who receive special education services, but it would allow parents to take a direct route (instead of a frustrating and unnecessarily devious route) to meet the definitions stated in the Education for the Handicapped Act.

Please contact me if you would like to discuss these answers to your questions, or if you would like to have additional information on the identification and treatment of ADD/ADHD.

Sincerely,

James M. Swanson, Ph.D.
Professor of Pediatrics, Psychiatry and Social Science
Director, UCI Child Development Center
Representative, Bloomingdale PGARD Group

APPENDIX C

The UCI-CDC Multicomponent Model

UCI-OCDE SCHOOL-BASED TREATMENT PROGRAM
FOR CHILDREN WITH ADHD/ODD

J SWANSON, S SIMPSON, D AGLER, R KOTKIN, L PFIFFNER, M BENDER,
C ROSENAU, K MAYFIELD, L FERRARI, L HOLCOMBE, D PRINCE, M
MORDKIN, J ELLIOT, S MIURA, C SHEA, S BONFORTE, D YOUPA, L
PHILLIPS, L NASH, K MCBURNETT, M LERNER, T ROBINSON, M LEVIN,
M BAREN, D CANTWELL

University of California and Orange County Department of Education
UCI Child Development Center, Department of Pediatrics
19262 Jamboree Road, Irvine, CA, USA 92715

INTRODUCTION

The most common treatment in the USA for Attention Deficit-Hyperactivity Disorder (ADHD) and Oppositional Defiant Disorder (ODD) is with stimulant medication[1,2], but even the manufacturer's instructions for using Ritalin (methylphenidate), the most frequently prescribed stimulant medication, recommend multimodality treatment[3]. The critical components of multimodality therapy have not been well-defined, but usually this means behavior therapy[4,5] (and sometimes psychotherapy and family therapy[6]) combined with stimulant therapy.

Investigations of the natural history of ADHD/ODD reveal a high risk for school failure, anti-social behavior and arrest[7,8,9]. Standard treatments with stimulant medication alone have not produced evidence of long-term effects on social adjustment[10,11,12] or academic achievement[13,14,15,16], but 2 recent evaluations of intensive multimodality treatment have provided limited empirical support for its effectiveness[12,17]. However, a series of reviews of the literature[5,15,17] identified some obvious issues (eg, intensity and duration of behavioral treatments, provisions for generalization training, combination of complementary treatments, and maintenance of treatments over time) which have not yet been adequately addressed to allow a fair evaluation.

Based on this literature, an intensive school-based treatment program was established in 1985 at Child Development Center (CDC) of the University of California, Irvine (UCI). The UCI-CDC program, which is not dependent on special education[18,19,20] funding, has evolved to include the 5 components described in this paper.

GENERAL PROGRAM CHARACTERISTICS

Target Patient Population

The entry criteria (described elsewhere[21]) require a diagnosis of ADHD or ODD, but extreme or "tip of the iceberg" cases are selected which usually have additional (or associated) diagnoses and represent the ADD-plus condition[22]. Referrals come primarily from a large (300 cases/year) UCI-CDC ADHD/ODD assessment clinic and private pediatric practices, which specialize in treating ADHD/ODD.

Funding for the Clinical Program

In the USA, public school funding for some clinical services for handicapped children (including those with "specific learning disabilities") has been legislated[18,20] and may be provided through special education programs. However, it is controversial whether ADHD/ODD should be recognized as a learning disability

171

under PL 94-142[20]. To avoid this controversy, a decision was made to fund the UCI-OCDE clinical program by health insurance and personal payments of clinical fees, which support the treatment staff employed by UCI [3 half-time psychologists (who supervise and coordinate the behavioral programs and work with parents), 3 counselors (who conduct the group therapy for social skills/ cognitive training), and 3 behavioral specialists (who extend the clinical intervention to the classroom)].

Funding for the Educational Component

Even for the educational component of the UCI-OCDE program, a decision was made to avoid special education[18,19,20] requirements and funding, due to entry restrictions (eg, IQ-achievement test discrepancy[19] requirements) and the cost of entitled non-educational benefits (eg, transportation). OCDE was authorized by the California State Department of Education to operate a model delinquency prevention program within its Juvenile Court School Program. In collaboration with UCI, a non-special education school-based intervention was designed for young children (under 12 years) with specific diagnoses (ADHD or ODD), who were not yet in trouble with the legal authorities but who were assumed to be "at-risk" for arrest[7,8,9]. Based on funding from average daily attendance rates for its Juvenile Court School, OCDE selected and assigned 3 teachers and a part-time principal to staff the special UCI-OCDE school. A small public school for up to 45 ADHD/ODD children was established in a 4,500 sq ft building on the UCI campus, with 3 classrooms to accommodate children between the ages of 5 to 11 years: a KG-Grade 1 class for ages 5 to 7, a Grade 2-3 class for ages 7 to 9, and a Grade 4-5 class for ages 9 to 11.

EMPIRICAL BASIS FOR THE 5 TREATMENT COMPONENTS

Intensive behavioral intervention in a special school setting

A school-based intervention was based on the literature which described behavioral treatment in special classrooms for disruptive children[23,24]. A long history of research [eg, from O'Leary[24,25,27] (at the SUNY Stony Brook Point of Woods Laboratory School) and from Pelham[5,17,26] (in summer treatment programs at Florida State University and the University of Pittsburgh)] has refined techniques for treating ADHD/ODD children in the classroom. These methods (described below) were imported by recruiting students of Pelham[26] and O'Leary[27] to be part of the treatment team.

The Levels System Linking Behavioral and Cognitive Group Therapy

Social skills training (SST)[17,26,28] and cognitive behavior therapy (CBT)[29,30,31,32] are provided in a group therapy setting, at a relatively high frequency (daily) and for a relatively long duration (for 1 year). Progress in the SST/CBT intervention is associated with movement through 3 levels of treatment. Level I intervention is based on continuous monitoring of and direct feedback to children using social reinforcers and tokens. An intensity sufficient to have an acute effect on the behavior of even difficult cases[17] is maintained (typically for 2 to 6 weeks) until success is achieved (defined as earning 90% of possible tokens). Level II intervention is based on self-monitoring and self-evaluation (the "match game"[25]), which is used to fade the continuous monitoring and is intended to foster generalization. The length of time to meet the criteria for matching with a counselor has been variable, requiring from 4 to 16 weeks. Level III intervention is based on self-evaluation using the "match game" and on responsibility/privilege contingencies which reflect the uncertainties of natural consequences in the real world environment. This has been used for long-term (24 to 48 week) maintenance of socially appropriate behavior without continuous use of tokens.

Generalization and transfer of SST/CBT training have been difficult to demonstrate[32]. To address this critical issue, specific generalization training is provided in 3 ways. Transfer across settings (from group therapy to the classroom) is fostered by mixing staff; the educational staff (teachers and aides) participate in cognitive and social skills training sessions, so they may act as discriminative stimuli and provide appropriate prompts in the classroom. Context-appropriate training is provided; cognitive techniques (eg, self-evaluation) are integrated into daily classroom and playground activities. Multiple token systems are linked; point values are equated and a common daily summary is used to make reinforcement contingent upon cross-situational behavior.

Long-term parent training

Six to 8 group sessions are scheduled to teach parents the basic principles and techniques of behavior modification[5,17,26,33,34]. In addition to this limited group contact, weekly individual meetings are scheduled for the parents with the psychologist who supervises the classroom and SST/CBT behavioral interventions. The purpose of these individual therapy sessions is to build mastery of behavioral techniques and to prepare parents to direct and maintain a permanent treatment program for the chronic residual symptoms that are expected to remain in ADHD/ODD children even after successful acute treatment[17,35].

Double-blind laboratory assessment of medication

In the USA the standard treatment of ADHD/ODD is with stimulant medication alone[12], but stimulants may be overused in the USA[36,37]. In the UCI-OCDE program only a minority of cases (about 30%) receive stimulant medication compared to the standard multimodality programs[6] in which close to 100% of the cases received stimulant medication. This minimal use of medication may be partially due to the application of a conservative procedure to assess cognitive response[36,37,38,39] before recommending the long-term use of medication. A double-blind dose-response assessment of cognitive response in the laboratory is conducted, which follows the advice of Sprague and Sleator[40] to check for cognitive toxicity. The literature on laboratory tests for documenting favorable effects has been reviewed elsewhere[36,37].

Transition experiences in a regular school setting

Some children in the UCI school-based treatment program enter a transition program in a designated public school [the El Toro Marine School (ETMS)]) for up to 3 months before placement in their neighborhood school. The interventions from the UCI-OCDE school are modified by UCI-ETMS team and in-service training is provided for teachers in the regular school environment (eg, a school token system with home-based rewards and a peer group for SST/CBT are established). The transition children are monitored in regular classroom and playground situations by the UCI-ETMS team.

SPECIFIC CHARACTERISTICS OF THE TOKEN ECONOMY

In the Classroom

In the UCI-OCDE school, students can earn token reinforcers (points) at the rate of 32 points/hour. Academic lessons (centers) are arranged in 30 minute blocks of time. A low student to staff ratio (7:1) is established to provide the structure and constant monitoring required to direct attention to academic tasks and to control the classroom behavior of extremely disruptive children. Every 30 minutes, a student can earn 16 points contingent on behavior in 5 areas: getting started (2 points), staying on task (4 points), interacting with peers and teacher (4 points), completing work (4 points), and stopping and cleaning up (2 points). Students start each 30 minute period with 16 points, and points are deducted for instances of behavior that violate the rules defined for each of these 5 classes of behavior. There is a point check at the end of each 30 minute period: children at Level I are given direct feedback of the number of points earned; children at Level II report their estimates of points earned and attempt to match with the teacher; children at Level III receive the maximum number of points if appropriate behavior was maintained. Each day a child completes 5 centers, so up to 80 points/day can be earned in the classroom in this interval-schedule response-cost program. An additional 5 points can be earned each day for completing homework.

In Group Therapy

A high density-reward system adapted from Pelham's work[5,17,26,38] is used to shape behavior and to build peer interaction skills in a group therapy setting. The token system for the SST/CBT group activity is based on a continuous schedule of praise and social reinforcement paired with continuous application of a token system covering the following positive and negative behaviors:

Points Earned		Points Lost	
1. Following directions	5	1. Interrupting	-10
2. Patience	5	2. Teasing	-10
3. Raising hand	5	3. Cursing	-10
4. Contributing	5	4. Refusing directions	-10
5. Staying with game	5	5. Namecalling	-10
6. Saying something nice	5	6. Being rude	-20
7. Solving a problem	10	7. Leaving the group	-30
8. Helping or sharing	10	8. Being aggressive	-50
9. Ignoring	15	9. Destroying property	-50
10. Bonus	5 to 15	10. Default	-10 to -50

In addition, every 10 minutes each child can earn points for the following 4 behaviors: following the rules (5 points), participating (5 points), being a good sport (15 points), and special category (15 points). Point checks are performed publicly; the counselor reviews for Level I children specifically why and how many points were earned (or lost) and asks each Level II and Level III child to perform a self-review.

After a 20 minute indoor session (which includes a review of the previous day's point totals, discussion of the topic of the day, and planning of group activity on the playground), the group practices the targeted skill or concept during a planned 20 minute outdoor activity (eg, a soccer game) while being monitored in the token

174

system. A review of this "reinforced practice" is conducted during the final 10 minute phase of the SST/CBT group session.

Across the hour SST/CBT session up to 320 points can be earned, so the continuous schedule of token reinforcement is about 10 times the rate of the interval schedule of the classroom (eg, 320/hour versus 32/hour). At the end of each session, the group therapy points are devalued (ie, divided by 10) to equate the actual rate in the two settings so a maximum of 32 program points are awarded.

Over the year of treatment, this standard methodology is used to shape behavior of children in different content areas or modules (eg, good sportsmanship, recognizing feelings, independence skills, appropriate assertion, problem solving, peer interaction), each of which may require from 1 to 6 weeks to complete. In Other Situations: Computer Drill, Lunch and Recess

Students can earn 16 points during a 30 minutes period of academic work on computers outside the classroom with a different teacher. Students can also earn 16 points during a 30 minute lunch/recess period when they eat in small groups and then select their own recess activities. A playground supervisor monitors behavior by using an interval schedule token system: every 2 to 4 minutes, children receive either 0, 1 or 2 points (2 points for cooperative play with another child, 1 point for solitary play, or 0 points for noncompliance with playground rules).

Backup (Activity) Reinforcement

At the end of the day, each child adds up the points earned across the classroom, SST/CBT, computer drill, lunch/recess and homework settings, and access to reinforcement is based on this daily total. Material reinforcers (eg, food or toys) are not used. Instead, the Premack Principle is applied and activity reinforcers are used. The "% earned" (of total possible points) is calculated by each child. Based on "% earned", 1 to 3 menus of activity reinforcers are made available during a 30 minute reinforcement period at the end of each day. Children who earn below 80% select from low priority activities (eg, reading a book, sitting quietly, drawing with a ruler or protractor); children who earn between 80% and 89% select from low or middle priority activities (eg, playing with clay, watching other children play computer games, drawing with crayons or felt pens, using the chalk board); children who earn 90% or more choose from low, middle or high priority activities (eg, playing computer games, using board games, working on special art projects). Daily point totals are accumulated across a 5 day period, and weekly activities at school (eg, video movie and popcorn) or elsewhere (eg, a trip to a park) are contingent upon this cumulative total.

LONG TERM PLANS

The UCI-OCDE school-based treatment program was established as a self-supporting clinical program to provide the intensity and duration of treatment that clinical experience, the literature, and basic principles of behavior therapy suggest may be required for long-term success of multimodality treatment. The 5 components of the treatment program described above define the type of program which may be evaluated to provide a rigorous and fair test of the effect of long-term intensive intervention with ADHD/ODD children.

REFERENCES

1. Cantwell D, Carlson G (1978) In: Werry J (ed) Pediatric Psycho-pharmacology. Bruner/Mazdel, New York
2. Amer Acad Ped (1975) Pediatrics 55:560-561
3. Physician's Desk Reference (1988) Medical Economics, Ordell,NJ
4. Werry JS, Wollersheim JP (1988) J Amer Acad Child Psych 28:1-18
5. Pelham W, Murphy H (1986) In: Herson N (ed) Pharmacological and Behavioral Treatment: An Integrative Approach. Wiley, New York
6. Satterfield J et al (1979) Arch Gen Psych 36: 965-974
7. Satterfield J at al (1982) Amer J Psych 139:795-798
8. Gittleman R et al (1985) Arch Gen Psych 42:937-947
9. Lambert N et al (1987) Amer J Orthopsychiat 57:22-32
10. Weiss G et al (1975) Canad Med Assn J 2:159-165
11. Riddle K, Rapport J (1976) J Nerv Ment Dis 162:126-134
12. Satterfield J et al (1987) J Amer Acad Child Psych 26:56-64
13. Barkley R (1977) J Child Psych Psychiat 18:137-165
14. Charles L, Shain R (1981) J Abnormal Child Psych 9:495-505
15. Pelham W (1983) Thalamus 3:1-47
16. Gadow K (1983) J Learn Disabilities 16:290-299
17. Pelham W (1988) In: Bloomingdale L (ed) Attention DeficitDisorder III. Pergamon, New York, pp 169-202
18. Education for All Handicapped Children Act (1975), PL 94-142, Sec 613(a)(4)
19. Forness S et al (1983) Learn Disabil Quart 6:107-114
20. Kavanagh J and Truss T (1988) In: Kavanagh J, Truss T (eds)Learning Disabilities: Proc.of the National Conf.York Press, Parkton MD, pp 549-551
21. Swanson J (1988) In: ibid, pp 532-546
22. Shaywitz S, Shaywitz B (1988) In: ibid, pp 369-523
23. Walker H, Buckley N (1972) J Applied Beh Anal 5:209-224.
24. O'Leary S, Schneider M (1977) Except Child Sept:24-30.
25. Turkewitz H et al (1975) J Consult Clin Psychol 43:577-583
26. Pelham W, Bender M (1982) In Gadow K (ed) Advances in Learning& Behavioral Disabilities. JAI Press, Greenwich CT, pp 365-436
27. Pfiffner L, O'Leary S (1987) J Appl Behav Anal 20:265-271
28. Oden S, Asher S (1977) Child Develop 48:495-506
29. Douglas V et al (1976) J Abnor Child Psychol 4:389-410
30. Hinshaw S et al (1984) J Consult Clin Psychol 52:739-749
31. Kendall P, Braswell L (1985) Cog.Behav. Ther. New York, Guilford Press
32. Whalen C et al (1985) J Abnor Child Psychol 13:391-410
33. Patterson G (1976) Families. Champaign, Research Press
34. Forehand R et al (1980) Behav Therapy 11:488-502
35. Pelham W (1989) In: Bloomingdale L and Swanson J (eds) Attention Deficit Disorder V. New York, Pergamon Press, pp
36. Swanson J (1989) In: ibid, pp
37. Swanson et al (in press) J Learn Disabil
38. Swanson et al (1978) Pediatrics 61:21-29
39. Swanson et al (1983) Pediatrics 72:49-55
40. Sprague R, Sleator E (1977) Science 198:1274-1276

APPENDIX D

The El Toro Elementary School Program for ADD Students

The Paraprofessional Model

Intervention Nomination

El Toro Marine Elementary School

Dan Graham, Principal

I. Description of the Practice

At El Toro Marine School, we have implemented a comprehensive behavior modification program specifically to deal with the special problems of children with Attention Deficit Disorder (ADD). The specific practices which have worked for us were taken from the model ADD school-based treatment program developed at the University of California, Irvine Child Development Center (UCI-CDC), which are described in 2 attached articles (Swanson, 1987; Swanson et al, 1990).

a. Need for School Interventions for ADD Students

Several years ago, the Irvine Unified School District (IUSD) recognized that the educational needs of some ADD students were not being met in the established placements within the IUSD. A collaboration was set up with the UCI-CDC to identify ADD children at the El Toro marine School, and to send the most seriously impaired students to the model school at the UCI-CDC which was designed specifically for ADD children. In return, the El Toro Marine School agreed to accept students from the UCI-CDC school after 1 year of treatment for a "transition program", to allow them to adapt to a regular school before returning to their home school. The transition program was so successful that the UCI-CDC and IUSD staffs decided to expand it to provide the initial 6 month to 1 year intensive ADD intervention at the El Toro Marine School site instead of transferring students to the UCI-CDC model school. This narrative describes the process we used to implement the specific practices to provide school intervention specifically for ADD students in the IUSD.

At the beginning of the 1990-1991 school year, we worked with Dr. James Swanson of the UCI-CDC to identify the need for an ADD intervention at El Toro. Based on teacher referrals and administrative (Principal and Psychologist) consultation, the parents of 21 students were interviewed by Dr. Swanson. This represented about 3.3% of the total student body of 600 elementary school aged children. Twelve of these 21 students were given diagnoses of Attention Deficit hyperactivity Disorder (ADHD) according to the DSM-III-R (1980) guidelines. These students entered a pilot program, funded by the IUSD, to implement the ADD practices described below.

At the beginning of the 1991-1992 school year, we started a replication of the initial pilot project. When we started this replication, new guidelines were available to define the need for programs to address the needs of ADD children in the public schools. The new Federal guidelines (Davila, Williams, and MacDonald, 1991) published by the Department of Education clearly recognized the need to provide educational intervention for ADD students. These new guidelines suggested two ways to deliver services to ADD students: in the regular education framework (under Section 504 of the Civil Rights Act) and in the special education framework (under the Individuals with Disabilities Education Act or IDEA).

The new Federal guidelines did not specify how many ADD children would be eligible for education services. At El Toro, the Principal (Dan Graham) and members of my school staff (Marsha Mortkin, the part-time school psychologist assigned to my school) surveyed all 660 students at the beginning of the 1991-1992 school year. We had experience in the prior year with the UCI staff (Ron Kotkin), who helped us use standard teacher questionnaires specifically related to ADD symptoms (the SNAP and CLAM).

Based on the teacher ratings, interviews with parents, and our extensive knowledge of day-to-day student problems and teacher complaints, in 1991-1992 we identified 18 students out of the 660 who had serious enough ADD symptoms to warrant intervention in our school. These 18 children (about 2.7% of the school's student body) were already experiencing significant problems in their classroom, and they accounted for a high percentage of discipline problems of the school. For example, one student was requiring 2 hours per day of the Principal's time, which was clearly unacceptable. This defined our need.

b. Goals and Objectives

The overall goal of the El Toro program was to use the spectrum of behavior modification and social skills practices (developed in the model school at the UCI-CDC) to meet the needs of our elementary school with a student body of about 600 children. Our specific objectives were the following:

(1) to modify two specific practices for use in the regular classroom. These 2 practices have been described as:

(a) a classroom intervention practice, called the parallel teaching practice, in which the teacher uses behavior o=modification techniques in parallel with the delivery of lesson plans for academic instruction. This practice is based on a well-established literature showing that positive attention ("catch 'em being good") and prudent negatives ("catch 'em before getting bad") work to control disruptive behavior of ADD children in the classroom. Behavior contracts and classroom token systems (daily reports) are used to formalize this process of

180

applying behavior modification principles and techniques in the classroom.

(b) the paraprofessional practice, in which an individual is trained to act as a classroom aide to focus on ADD students in the classroom who need a greater frequency and intensity of positive attention and prudent negatives than the teacher alone could provide, as well as to act a a group leader in small groups designed to teach social (cooperation, communication, participation, and validation) and cognitive (self-monitoring and self-evaluation) skills which ADD children typically lack.

(2) to set up the 2 practices (behavior modification via parallel teaching, and paraprofessional intervention) at the El Toro school to serve ADD students on-site.

(3) to assign the practices to meet the needs of the 18 ADD students.

c. The "How to" of Implementing the Practices.

Our experience informed us that not all of the 21 ADD children would have an educational impairment serious enough to require services considered to be special education services. The school psychologist (Marsha Mortkin) and counselor (David Prince) trained the teachers to use 2 standard behavior modification techniques described by Pfiffner and Barkley (1990):"

(1) "behavior contracts" (to deal with disruptive behavior on the playground). The school counselor (Dave Prince) targeted specific behaviors which had a history of disrupting recess and lunch time. These behaviors were written down for the child and the outside supervision, and a simple chart was constructed which was completed by the outside supervisor on a daily basis. The charts were returned to David Prince, who used activities (time on the computer, school duties, etc) as reinforcers.

(2) "daily reports" (associated with a token system targeting deportment and academic performance in the classroom). The El Toro staff (teachers, psychologist, counselor, and principal) adapted the UCI-CDC classroom token system (which required feedback after every class period) for use on a less frequent (eg., daily) basis.

The behavior contracts and daily reports were considered to be modifications to the regular classroom environment. No additional resources, other than staff training and administrative support, were provided at this level of intervention. To prepare for the more difficult ADD students who would be unable to remain in a classroom of 30 children with 1 teacher, the El Toro staff imported and adapted the "paraprofessional" model from UCI-CDC.

The paraprofessional practice at El Toro was designed and supervised by

Dr. Ron Kotkin. He identified a college student who had been trained in the UCI-CDC school-based day-treatment program. This student was hired for 19 hour per week by the Irvine Unified School District, and assigned to the ADD project at El Toro Marine School. Supervision was provided by Dr. Kotkin, who also trained the school psychologist to work with the paraprofessional. The school psychologist arranged the schedule for two components of the paraprofessional practice:

(1) a "pull out" component, in which the paraprofessional has twice-a-week small group training to teach social and cognitive skills;

(2) a classroom component, in which the paraprofessional spends 12 hours per week as an instructional aide in the classroom to supplement the teacher who agreed to take the 2 seriously impaired ADD students.

During the 1990-1991 school year, we contrasted groups of ADD children who received either the social skills practice alone (SS Only) or both of these practices at the same time (SS + Classroom Aide), with a group of ADD who were not assigned to one of these school interventions (Control).

II. Outcome

The results of the 1990-1991 study contrasted use of the 2 practices (SS Only versus SS + Classroom Aide). A composite scores indicated that all of the students receiving the combined set of practices (SS + Classroom Aide) improved over the course of the year, while less than half of the students in the control group or the SS only group improved. Specific scores related to ADD (or "disruptive") behavior revealed that the decrease in disruptive behavior was large (over a 50% decline) in the students receiving both practices, but either small (less than a 20% decline in the SS Only group) or in the opposite direction (over a 15% increase in the Control group).

Interviews with the teachers during the next (1991-1992), when the students were no longer in a special intervention program, revealed an even more impressive impact on student in the SS + Classroom aide group. One student, who was regularly spent to the Principal's office 2 to 4 time per week before the 1990-1991 program of intervention, had been referred to the Principal only 2 times in 5 months. The other students were still in their initial 1991-1992 classroom placements, and despite some minor problems, were rated as having adequate or better performance in their classes.

III. Replication

a. Old (El Toro) and New (Deerfield) Sites

The initial pilot project was so successful that the IUSD funded an expansion of the program for the 1991-1992 year. The identification of students at El Toro (described above) was duplicated at another school (Deerfield Elementary School). John Brady, Ph.D., a Program Specialists in the IUSD, and Ron Kotkin, Ph.D., of the UCI-CDC, supervised the identification of students and the training of the staff at Deerfield. Thus, the replication of the initial application of the "paraprofessional" practice (the combined of the SS + Classroom Aide practices) was designed to replicate the El Toro model at the same site (El Toro) and at a new site (Deerfield). Only the replication at El Toro will be described here.

b. El Toro Replication

For the 1991-1992 school year, another pilot project was funded by t he IUSD. This included only the combined practice (SS + Classroom Aide) for students with extreme ADD symptoms. The ADD students with less serious problems received specific alterations in the classroom environment without the addition of extra resources. The methods of identification of these ADD students are described above in the needs section. Based on those methods, 18 students (2.7% of the El Toro student body) were identified.

Of the 18 ADD students identified by the school staff, 12 responded very well to the "behavior contracts" and the "daily reports". The key to the effective use of these practices was teacher training (supervised by Marsha Mortkin, the school psychologist, with consultation from the UCI-CDC staff) and the establishment of a positive incentive program (supervised by Dave Prince, the school counselor) to replace the school's "assertive discipline" policy which did not work with these children. The assertive discipline program is essentially a "response cost" program, in which students are sequentially warned for the first few instances of rule violation, and finally sent to the principal's office if the behavior continues. We found that ADD children do not respond well to this type intervention which technically is "punishment" in the behavior modification framework. The "behavior contracts" and "daily reports" were established to emphasize positive incentive programs, instead of negative punishments programs. This worked very well for over half of our identified ADD students.

The simple and easy to use interventions described above ("behavior contracts" and "daily reports") were not successful in 6 of the 18 ADD subjects we identified at the El Toro Marine School. These ADD students had serious problems which already required the excessive time and attention of the teacher and the principal. These students were showing normal or expected achievement levels on psychological tests, but their performance in the classroom (based on compliance and work completed correctly) was very low — below the 25% percentile.

We assigned the 4 seriously impaired ADD students to the replication of the "paraprofessional" intervention program. Two teachers were selected, and 2 ADD students were assigned to each of 2 classrooms. As described above, to get a teacher to accept these "problems children", we hired a college student trained at the UCI-CDC and assigned that "paraprofessional" as an extra teachers' aide to work in the classroom. The paraprofessional had already been trained at UCI-CDC

183

to do the following:

1. How to deliver a skills remediation component in a twice-a-week group meeting with the 3 ADD students. To conduct this group, the paraprofessional must be trained to use a continuous reinforcement system to shape new social skills and cognitive behaviors (Ironsmith et al, 1978).

2. How to work as a teacher's aide in the classroom to help implement a token economy. In this token or "point system", the new social and cognitive skills developed in the skill remediation group are elicited and reinforced in the natural environment of the regular classroom. A point system was established for each class period, and the paraprofessional supervised frequent monitoring (by awarding points every period) and application of reinforcers (access to preferred activities on a daily basis).

In the 4 ADD cases assigned to the paraprofessional practice, the frequency and intensity of the behavior modification program (describe above) has been (so far) sufficient to attain a high (eg., 90%) degree of appropriate behavior in the classroom. This was expected from the work at UCI-CDC and from the literature (eg., Walker and Buckley, 1972). The magnitude of the effects of the replication seem to be at least as great as the initial pilot presented earlier.

b. Multiple Input Approach

After trying the parallel teaching practice (contracts and daily reports) and the paraprofessional practice (twice a week groups, and extra time for a classroom aide), we still found that 2 of the 18 ADD students were seriously impaired in their school performance. These 2 children required an inordinate amount of individual attention from the principal and the teacher. In addition, staff time spent with parents (telephone calls, early pick-up arrangements, etc) was required.

The El Toro Marine School did not attempt to implement practices to serve these 2 ADD children. Instead, the school staff contacted the parents and recommended the UCI-CDC school-based treatment program. Letters were written to the insurance carrier (Champus), with supportive material from the Family Services Group at the El Toro Marine Base, to obtain funding for the clinical component of the UCI-CDC program. This allowed extensive work with the parents, as well as more structure, closer monitoring, and a greater frequency and intensity of reinforcers. The staff considered this placement to be temporary, with an expectation of the student returning the El Toro Marine School within a 1 year period of time.